THE TRANSFORMING SYSTEM:

A PRACTICAL HANDBOOK FOR UNDERSTANDING THE CHANGES IN CALIFORNIA COMMUNITY MENTAL HEALTH

The American Association for Marriage and Family Therapy is the national professional association for the field of marriage and family therapy. We represent the professional interests of more than 50,000 marriage and family therapists throughout the United States, Canada and abroad. Our association facilitates research, theory development and education. We develop standards for graduate education and training, clinical supervision, professional ethics and the clinical practice of marriage and family therapy.

AAMFT: BECAUSE A PROFESSION IS MORE THAN A LICENSE.

American Association for Marriage & Family Therapy
California Division
P.O. Box 6907
Santa Barbara, CA 93160
www.aamftca.org

TABLE OF CONTENTS

ACKNOWLEDGEMENTS

The Fabulous Four

The Handbook that follows is the outcome of a truly collaborative process. First and foremost, the credit for this work goes to the same amazing women who served on the AAMFT-CA Division Course Development Committee and produced The Transformed Supervisor training course:

Margaret Avineri, Psy.D., LMFT, is the Senior Director of Clinical & Community Support Services at Jewish Family Service of Los Angeles (JFSLA). Particularly interested in mentoring new and emerging clinicians, she has taught Legal & Ethical Aspects of Counseling and Practicum in the MFT program at California State University Dominguez Hills, and Family Therapy, Supervision and Law & Ethics courses in other academic and professional settings. Margaret's early training and work experience as a social worker in rural Israel strongly influenced her commitment to advocating for social services that are integrated and client-centered. In her administrative capacity at JFSLA and as an AAMFT Approved Supervisor, she has developed a special interest in the role of training in non-profit agencies and the public mental health system. She is delighted to participate in the collaborative creation of a course for "Transformed Supervisors" and the subsequent "Transforming System" Handbook.

Susan Davis, M.S., LMFT, is currently the MFT Intern Program Supervisor for the Department of Behavioral Health at the County of San Bernardino. She has worked in public mental health for eighteen years both in California and in the State of Washington. Prior to her work in public mental health she was in private practice in Southern California for thirteen years. She has been an adjunct professor in the psychology graduate program at Chapman University in Washington State. She is a licensed MFT and an AAMFT approved supervisor. Her work in public mental health has created a deeper understanding of the mental health needs in the public sector and an appreciation of the components of Recovery-oriented Care. She finds working with MFT trainees and interns to be both enjoyable and gratifying and being a part of the development of this training and Handbook to have been a rewarding experience.

Mary M. Read, Ph.D., LMFT is the Director of Clinical Training for the MS in Counseling program at California State University, Fullerton, where she has taught since 1990. Maintaining a small clinical practice, she enjoys the interactive flow of teaching classes, networking with practicum agencies and alumni, doing research, seeing clients, and mentoring interns. She is a co-chair of the MFT Regional Consortium of Orange County, and participates in a number of state-wide committees through AAMFT and CAMFT that provide leadership to the ever-evolving field of Marriage & Family

therapy in California. Participating with the team in developing and delivering the Transformed Supervisor course and this handbook has been a highly enjoyable experience.

Kathy Wexler, M.A., LMFT is the Department Chair of the Marriage and Family Therapy Program at Phillips Graduate Institute in Chatsworth. She has been on the faculty since 1978, and has also served as a clinical supervisor in Phillips' California Family Counseling Center. She is a longtime AAMFT clinical member and Approved Supervisor. Kathy is also known as a trainer for the BBS licensing exams, having offered workshops through AATBS since 1978. She is excited to be part of developing training and education for the new recovery paradigm.

The Committee gives special thanks to Kathy Wexler who provided the impetus for this project. As Department Chair of the Marriage and Family Therapy Program, Phillips Graduate Institute, she was struggling to find relevant resources to incorporate into their revised curriculum before August 2012. Being a part of the creative team that produced the **Transformed Supervisor** training, it was Kathy who first pushed us to expand the course's extensive Participant Workbook into a text that could be used in her graduate school classrooms. Kathy's belief in the relevance and practical value of such a text encouraged us to move quickly in order to have it ready for educators by Fall Semester, 2012.

When the Committee agreed to take on yet another project, the Fabulous Four proceeded with the same tireless energy, good nature and truly gracious and giving spirit that encompassed the creation of the **Transformed Supervisor** training course. The working process was energized by honest exchange, support, competency and mutual encouragement. Educators, students, the California public mental health system and AAMFT-CA Division will all benefit from the dedication and work of these outstanding professional leaders.

A Collaborative Effort

Beyond the work of the AAMFT-CA Development Committee members, a number of dedicated individuals, educational institutions and community agencies contributed material to enrich and broaden the scope of the Handbook. With a gracious and generous "community" spirit, our collaborators were eager to share their knowledge for this purpose and very responsive in submitting their work. Many thanks go out to:

Boundaries and Ethical Considerations

Alliant International University

Steve Brown, PhD, JD

Marcia Michaels, PsyD

Benjamin Caldwell, PsyD

Linna Wang, PhD

Direct from the Employers

- Bonita House

  » Rick Crispino, Executive Director

- Casa Pacifica Centers for Children and Families

  » Steve Elson, PhD, Chief Executive Officer

- Child and Family Center, Santa Clarita

  » Larry Schallert, LCSW, Director of Program Development

  » Roberta Rubin, PhD, Outpatient Community Services Director

  » Darrell Paulk, Chief Executive Officer

- Didi Hirsch Mental Health Services

  » Kita Curry, PhD, Chief Executive Officer

- Foothill Family Service

  » Helen Morran-Wolf, LCSW, Chief Executive Officer

- Jewish Family Service of Los Angeles

  » Carolyn Heier, PsyD, Director of DMH Programs

  » Paul S. Castro, JD, Chief Executive Officer

- Los Angeles County Department of Mental Health

  » Robin Kay, PhD, Chief Deputy Director

  » Marvin Southard, DSW, Director

- Sanctuary Psychiatric Centers of Santa Barbara

  » Lisa Moschini, LMFT, Clinical Director

  » Barry R. Schoer, Executive Director

- Turning Point of Central California
    - » Wally Parks, LMFT, Regional Director
    - » J. Jeff Fly, MA, Chief Executive Officer

Direct from the Consumers
Renee C
Maria V
Faith I
Linda B
Kristen S
Michael M
Michelle S
Alberto O
Joseph C
Christian B
Lydia A
LaVerne
Vivian L
Emilia A
William N
Virginia M
Jerry S
Mayra G

Quick Tips to Strengthen the Provide-Client Relationship through Cultural Understanding
Center for Integrated Health Solutions, SAMSHA-HRSA

Preparing for the Future: Fitting Into the Vision
Rebecca Wrighton, MA

Book Design
Shareena Yee

A special acknowledgement goes to **Dana Stone, Ph.D.** and **Diane Gehart, Ph.D.**, for the section they co-authored, titled: **A Strengths-Based, Postmodern Approach to Recovery-Oriented Therapy with Persons Diagnosed with Severe Mental Illness.** Diane's long-term, ongoing support, encouragement, enthusiasm and selfless participation in AAMFT-CA Division projects and programs for educators and students have continually provided outstanding guidance to our professional community. Diane is truly a gift to our profession and we also look forward to great things from Dr. Stone.

It is the willingness to share and participate on the part of those listed above that turned this Handbook from a concept into a reality. AAMFT-CA Division is grateful to all.

Olivia Loewy, Ph.D.

Executive Director

AAMFT-CA Division

Olivia Loewy, Ph.D., is the Executive Director of the California Division of the American Association for Marriage and Family Therapy (AAMFT-CA). Olivia also represents the interests of MFTs at a state level through her active involvement with the California Council of Community Mental Health Agencies (CCCMHA), the California Institute of Mental Health (CIMH) Policy Forum Planning Committee, the Mental Health Services Act (MHSA) Education and Training Unit and the California Coalition for Whole Health (CCWH). Olivia is a licensed MFT and an AAMFT Approved Supervisor. Prior to her current position, she served for 10 years as the Clinical Director at Verdugo Mental Health in Glendale, CA. She considers her years as a supervisor and trainer in the public system among the best, and participating in the development of the Transformed Supervisor course and the Transforming Systems Handbook has been a joy.

INTRODUCTION

California Community Mental Health is in the midst of an evolutionary transformation process. The President's New Freedom Commission report, published in 2003, included recommendations that called for sweeping changes in the way that public mental health care was delivered throughout the country. The Commission report began with a Vision Statement that referenced a "recovery orientation" to care. One year later, California became the first (and so far only) state in the nation to pass a ballot initiative that designated the collection of tax monies to be specifically used to transform the public mental health system. Proposition 63 was the ballot initiative that became a law known as the Mental Health Services Act (MHSA) in January 2005. The MHSA embodied those recommendations presented in the New Freedom Commission report.

Transformation of an established government-directed system is a long, encompassing and slow-moving process. Multiple layers of process, procedure and people are affected. Change pertaining to the delivery of care began with management in a process aimed at transforming the treatment culture throughout all levels of providers and participants.

To ensure a cohesive system, the California Board of Behavioral Sciences sponsored Senate Bill 33 – legislation that was passed in 2009 with a designated implementation date of August, 2012. Senate Bill 33 required Marriage and Family Therapy graduate school curriculum to incorporate the concepts and approach to treatment contained in the MHSA. This law not infrequently required educators and supervisors to learn an orientation to treatment that they had never previously been taught. Senate Bill 33 also inadvertently imposed a readiness requirement on clinical supervisors who would be working with the new graduate students now prepared for employment in the transformed system.

In response to an unmet training need within the California public mental health system, the American Association for Marriage and Family Therapy, California Division (AAMFT-CA Division) developed a course for clinical supervisors that focused on the recovery orientation to care, titled: **The Transformed Supervisor: *Clinical Supervision in California Public Mental Health*.** Course participants received an 80-page workbook that contained articles and resources about the changes in the system and the subsequent clinical implications. Because some clinical supervisors are also educators, AAMFT-CA began to receive requests to utilize **The Transformed Supervisor** Participant Workbook as the basis for a student text that could be made available for MFT graduate school courses in the revised curriculum. The resulting textbook now lies in your hands.

The Transforming System: A Practical Handbook for Understanding the Changes in California Community Mental Health is a brief and very practical text. Multiple contributors engaged in a collaborative process to bring this information to you: clinicians, managers, educators, employers and consumers all contributed to the contents of this handbook.

Although the handbook refers to "Community" Mental Health in California, the contributors are aware that the scope of this publication does not represent every provider of mental health services in the state. There are many agencies that provide mental health services---at a grass-roots level, in medical clinics and in locally funded organizations as well as in larger DMH-contracted and directly operated agencies. While the recovery model is particularly relevant and prevalent in DMH-funded programs, the shift in perspective that accompanies the recovery orientation is also finding its way into all types of organizations and training programs throughout the state. This handbook, therefore, provides a useful overview of recovery-oriented care for any clinician-in-training in a wide variety of treatment settings.

The evolution of this handbook has been and will be a continuous and dynamic process. As the information in this text requires updates, new editions will be released. For now, the content is current, relevant and visionary. Our hope is that this material will provide a solid foundation, a useful perspective and valuable guidance to take you into the future.

PART ONE
EVOLVING SYSTEMS OF CARE

- Healthcare Reform: The Big Picture

- California: Leading the Nation with MHSA

- Bringing It Home: County and Community

THE BIG PICTURE

Olivia Loewy, Ph.D.

In the Beginning

On April 29, 2002, President Bush announced that three obstacles were preventing Americans with mental illness from getting the excellent care they deserve:

- Stigma that surrounds mental illness

- Unfair treatment limitations and financial requirements placed on mental health benefits in private health insurance, and

- The fragmented mental health service delivery system.

Subsequently, the President's New Freedom Commission was established and charged to study the mental health service delivery system and to make recommendations that would enable adults with serious mental illnesses and children with serious emotional disturbance to live, work, learn and participate fully in their communities.

The Commission's report, published in July 2003, began with the following Vision Statement:

> We envision a future when everyone with a mental illness will recover, a future when mental illnesses can be prevented or cured, a future when mental illnesses are detected early, and a future when everyone with a mental illness at any stage of life has access to effective treatment and supports – essentials for living, working, learning and participating fully in the community.

The bulk of the report was based on the underlying premise that: "To improve access to quality care and services, the Commission recommends fundamentally transforming how mental health care is delivered in America."

The key to a transformed system was designated as recovery and six goals were identified as the foundation for transforming mental health care in America:

Goal 1: Americans Understand that Mental Health is Essential to Overall Health.

Goal 2: Mental Health Care is Consumer and Family Driven.

Goal 3: Disparities in Mental Health Services are Eliminated.

Goal 4: Early Mental Health Screening, Assessment, and Referral to Services are Common Practice.

Goal 5: Excellent Mental Health Care is Delivered and Research is Accelerated.

Goal 6: Technology is used to Access Mental Health Care and Information.

This Commission, and the report that it produced, were the beginning of a movement at the federal level that would affect subsequent policy, legislation and funding.

Transformation in Process

Almost 10 years later, those recommendations proposed in 2003 are in implementation stages nationally, taking the form of new systems of care and pilot projects that have emerged at the state level throughout the country.

Truly massive change has occurred. It has been slow and sometimes awkward, but the forces of change continue to move us forward. The movement has been consistently fueled by research that is serving to alter the shape of the transforming system. Most notably, data pertaining to the increased and advanced health problems and premature deaths that have been identified within the seriously mentally ill (SMI) population irrefutably lead to the conclusion that to continue to "separate the head from the body" results in ineffective, inefficient and costly delivery of care.

Don Berwick, when he was Director of the Center for Medicare and Medicaid Services (CMS) presented a formulation to guide evolving systems of care called the **Triple Aim**: Better Health; Better Care Experience; Lower Cost.

Emerging transformed systems of care have been shaped by comprehensive research and inspired by the Triple Aim. Fundamental tenets of service delivery have surfaced:

- Care is **integrated**.
- Care is **accountable**.
- Services are **consumer-driven**.

Integrated Care

What is integrated care? It is a system of care that is comprehensive, coordinated and multidisciplinary. It is designed to treat the whole person.

Systems of integrated care are in developmental stages and take a multitude of forms. However to be considered "integrated," the system must incorporate both primary and behavioral health care. Primary care refers to traditional medical services. Behavioral healthcare includes both mental health and substance abuse treatment. Across the country pilot projects and initial integrated systems of care sometimes encompass dental and vision services. Some systems extend into the realm of typical community services, such as case management, employment counseling or short-term solution-focused therapy. The **recovery** model concepts of service provision that provide "whatever it takes" and encourage entry into the system through "no wrong door" have guided the development of the more extensive structures of care.

In response to comprehensive, multi-dimensional systems of care, the concept of a "Medical Home" emerged. "Medical Home" refers to a person or a provider team that takes responsibility for overseeing and coordinating the individual's treatment. The Medical Home is an integral part of a system designed to treat the whole person. Depending on how the system of care is designed, Medical Home assessments could involve the individual's family, teacher, case worker, counselor, and significant others. The Medical Home is the repository for all relevant information about the patient, such as medical history, medications, mental health treatment, and relational or economic stressors. This comprehensive information promotes coordination and guides communication.

Integrated care might be housed in one location or coordinated so that services are provided in different locations but remain within the same system. Diverse structures, systems and procedures have been created in response to predictable questions and considerations that often involve issues related to: location; number and discipline of providers; merging behavioral and primary care cultures; record-keeping and documentation; confidentiality; assessment instruments and methods; billing and financial regulations; liability; outcome indicators and measurement methods.

The staffing and provider structure also takes a diversity of forms within emerging systems of care. Some structures included a multi-disciplinary in-house team within the behavioral health component of services. Thus a social worker, MFT, licensed professional counselor, and substance abuse counselor, might all be on staff and called on to provide treatment that requires the area of expertise associated with each discipline. In some of these settings, MFTs are referred to as Medical Family Therapists.

Integrated care is complex. Developing structures of integrated care require tackling complicated issues related to coordination and communication. Answers to structural questions that surface during the construction of new systems reveal the knowledge, skills, values and fears of those in charge. The developmental process is a creative one and a "tried and true", universally accepted set

of blueprints has yet to be developed.

As healthcare systems continue to evolve, "best practices" will emerge and accepted guidelines will become established. For now, the concept of integrated care is strong and compelling enough to generate ongoing attempts to fulfill the promise that it holds and the merging of behavioral and primary care is fundamental within the developing structures.

Linda Rosenberg, President and CEO, National Council for Community Behavioral Healthcare, puts the broad concept of integrated care into a very practical perspective that ties together treatment and economic efficiency as she states: "Integration isn't a concept: it's a way of doing business." She further states: "Healthcare of the future is data-driven. Care is increasingly transparent and the results of care increasingly public."

Accountable Care

Accountable care means that research, measurement techniques and outcome indicators will be utilized to shape the emerging systems. Best practices will be determined by the results of this research and the subsequent assessments that are conducted.

The President's New Freedom Commission's goals and recommendations were turned into action steps in part because research has compellingly highlighted the need for change and presented encompassing data tied to cost. The statistics that conclusively linked advanced medical complications and premature deaths to the seriously mentally ill (SMI) populations impelled us into models of comprehensive care designed to treat the whole person. Beyond the costs associated with inferior and insufficient medical care for the SMI population, our neglect of primary preventative care has resulted in a national system of healthcare that is needlessly costly.

In relation to dollars, Dale Jarvis, nationally known healthcare management consultant, has stated:

> Money only flows in large quantities after you get sick for services designed to 'fix what is broken.' Prevention, primary care, and behavioral health are dramatically underfunded in the U.S. and health insurance dollars are rarely used to promote the health of the population. The U.S. now spends more than twice per person what other industrialized countries do and has some of the worst outcomes. This sick care system is unsustainable for the federal government, states, businesses, and individuals.

At the federal level, in 2011, CMS proposed a system of "bundled care" financing in which reimbursement is provided for "episodes" of treatment and not for "pieces" of care. It is becoming increasingly clear that to function most efficiently, integrated systems of care will require new methods of billing that can accommodate the coordinated, multi-disciplinary approach to service delivery. The new term that has found its way into health economists' vocabulary is "paying for value, not volume".

Accountable care means that performance is public. It challenges managers and providers to agree that improvements in our systems are needed and to join together in documented and transparent attempts to initiate change. Accountable care is not a "punishing" concept – it is all about learning and building and improving upon the work of others.

Beyond saving dollars, accountable care is about saving lives. Both process and outcome are reviewed. Indicators are designed to explore system efficiency and access to care, assessment and treatment processes, follow-up procedures and client satisfaction. Client subjective experience and satisfaction measures are a critical part of accountable care because in the evolving systems, services are consumer driven.

Services are Consumer-driven

The President's Commission report stated that the key to a transformed system of healthcare can be found within the principles of the concepts related to **recovery**. In the development of systems of Recovery-oriented Care, mental health is leading the way and pushing new procedures into integrated structures.

Kenneth S. Thompson, M.D., Chief Medical Officer, Recovery Innovations and Associate Professor of Psychiatry and Public Health, University of Pittsburgh and Western Psychiatric Institute and Clinic, states:

> …..the primary advocate has been the consumer movement and the purpose has been to dramatically change the relationship between persons with psychiatric challenges and those who want to help them. This in turn changes the nature of practice from being that of treating people to supporting them in their recovery process. There are technical tools, like protocols for shared decision making or wellness and recovery action plans, but these largely exist to support the fundamental change in the nature of the healing relationship. This is a new platform for practice.

Consumer driven procedures and practices are inclusive and respectful. The expertise of patients in relation to their knowledge of their own feelings, behaviors, compliance potential, motivation and resources is a valued part of the initial and ongoing assessment process. Treatment becomes a joint process and responsibility is shared.

From a practical perspective, for treatment decisions and responsibility to be truly a shared process, concerns about liability must be addressed and accommodating billing structures must be developed so as to provide a safe and comfortable framework within which recovery-oriented care can be delivered.

In mental health, consumer-driven services require the development of a new kind of therapeutic relationship. Traditional boundaries are challenged as the 50-minute session in a therapist's office turns into the delivery of services out in the community, on a bus or in the street. Care is provided as needed, whether preventative or reactive. The consumer's own assessment of need is acknowledged and supported. The medical model turns into a practice of shared expertise and the consumer – and sometimes family members—are an active part of the decision making process as related to ongoing or revised treatment plans.

John S. Kern, M.D., Chief Medical Officer, Regional Mental Health Center, presents his view of the future as follows:

> …My view of the future of behavioral healthcare? On the one hand, getting organized, being systematic, counting things, and functioning as a team seems to help. On the other hand, we return as always to the importance of the personal caring relationship. Any future model of care will eventually succeed to the extent that it provides support to this kind of contact with the people we serve.

In some emerging systems of care, consumers are sought out to become part of the staff and actively participate in treatment teams. Mental health transformation in the public sector is being led by the state of California, where the passage of Proposition 63 in 2004 became a law in 2005 known as the Mental Health Services Act.

Reference

National Council for Community Behavioral Healthcare: *National Council Magazine*: 2012, Issue 1.

Discussion Questions:

1. What is your image of how mental illness was treated in the United States 30 or 40 years ago?

2. Do you believe that Integrated Care will become the norm? Why? What would need to happen before this encompassing change can take place?

3. Should funding for the public mental health system be tied to measurable outcomes? If so, what should be measured?

4. Will the Recovery Orientation make mental health providers more or less "professional?" Why?

5. How does expertise in Marriage and Family Therapy fit into the new structures of care?

SELECTED READINGS AND MATERIALS ON RECOVERY

California Board of Behavioral Sciences. Mental health recovery reference guide.

    http://www.bbs.ca.gov/pdf/mhsa/resource/recovery/recovery_reference_guide.pdf

    Also available at http://www.mhrecovery.com

Hamilton County OH Department of Mental Health

    http://www.mhrecovery.com

Federal Government Resources and info:

    http://www.mentalhealth.samhsa.gov

Mary Ellen Copeland, author

    http://www.mentalhealthrecovery.com

MHA Village of Los Angeles

    http://www.mhavillage.squarespace.com

National Association of Social Workers. NASW Practice Snapshot: The mental health recovery model

    http://www.socialworkers.org/practice/behavioral_health/0206snapshot.asp

Substance Abuse and Mental Health Services Administration (Federal resource)

    http://www.mentalhealth.samhsa.gov

Web-Accessible References and Resources for more information on MHSA:

- The Annapolis Coalition on the Behavioral Health Workforce

- California Council of Community Mental Health Agencies (http://www.cccmha.org): Proposition 63: How Did it Happen?

- California DMH/SQIC: IOM Quality Chasm Principles and Rules for Behavioral Health

- California Mental Health Financing 101: Patricia Ryan, Executive Director, California Mental Health Directors Association

- California Mental Health Funding: Evolution and Policy Implications, Pre and Post MHSA

- The California Mental Health Services Act Stakeholder Process: Issues and Approaches.

- California's Mental Health System – Underfunded from the Start

- California Primary Care, Mental Health, and Substance Use Services Integ., ration Policy Initiative

- The Campaign for Mental Health Reform

  » Inclusion of Mental Healthcare in Overall Healthcare Reform

- CMHDA Principles for Mental Health Services Act (MHSA) Implementation

- Crossing the Quality Chasm: Institute of Medicine

- EMQ Families First: Facts about EMQ Families First Wraparound Program

- From Fail-First to Help-First – Proposition 63 Transforms California's Mental Health System

  » Preliminary implementation guide prepared by and for California Council of Community Mental Health Agencies by Rusty Selix, Executive Director, CCCMHA and official co-proponent and co-author of Proposition 63- together with Assemblyman Darrell Steinberg.

- From Promise to Practice: Mental Health Models that Work for Children and Youth

- Implementing Proposition 63, the Mental Health Services Act, with Vision and Purpose by Mark Ragins, M.D.

- Key Issues for Community Mental Health Agencies and First Steps for Department of Mental Health Implementation

- The President's New Freedom Commission on Mental Health

- Summary of the Mental Health Services Act

- USPRA (U.S. Psychiatric Rehabilitation Association): Lessons Learned from California's A.B. 2034 Programs

  » Part II: Looking Back

  » Conclusion: Lessons Learned

    * Principal Author: Shannon Mong. Contributing Authors: Beth Conley and Dave Pilon

    * A Wish List of Broken Rules by Mark Ragins, M.D.

CALIFORNIA LEADING THE NATION WITH MHSA: THE MENTAL HEALTH SERVICES ACT: HISTORY, COMPONENTS, PROMISE AND CHALLENGES

Olivia Loewy, Ph.D.

Historical Overview: California Mental Health Funding

The delivery of public mental health services in California was first significantly altered by legislation that began more than 50 years ago. In 1957, the California public mental health system was operating 8 state hospitals, serving over 36,000 people when the Short Doyle Act was passed, which encouraged counties to develop community mental health programs. Nearly a decade later, in 1967 the Lanterman Petris Short (LPS) Act increased state funding for some mental health programs and started the process of converting California's hospital-based mental health system to community care. The legislation included a promise that the money would follow the clients into an adequately funded community care system; however, this promise was not fulfilled until almost 40 years later with the passage of Proposition 63 in 2004.

In the meantime, underfunded mental health services created a crisis of unmet need in the communities. In the 1970s and 80s, state allocations to counties were severely diminished due to inflation and funding reductions and by 1990, California faced a $15 billion state budget shortfall, which would have resulted in more cuts to mental health. This crisis led to the 1991 enactment of Realignment with the passage of the Bronzan-McCorquodale Act. Realignment provided a flow of revenues directly to counties, generated from a ½ cent increase in state sales tax and state vehicle license fees. The Realignment formula is flawed as a dependable source of mental health funds in that it includes social services programs that are entitlements and are given priority for growth. Because of the social services program priorities, no sales tax growth was received in mental health for several years, and only a small amount in FY 2005 -06. Mental health, furthermore, is expected to receive reduced amounts of sales tax growth, if any, for the foreseeable future.

Federal Medicaid (MediCal) provides the second largest revenue source for county mental health programs. MediCal services have also not grown and require counties to use Realignment funds to pay for increased cost of living adjustments. Despite all of the struggles for adequate funding and efforts to increase services, in early 2000, it was estimated that the California public mental health system was serving only about 40% of people with serious, disabling mental illness. California ranks near the bottom nationally in resources available for persons receiving Medicaid. Polls of California voters showed significant support for expanded service and in 2003, 82% of those polled responded

that if people with severe mental illness were not getting needed treatment, it was a serious problem.

Proposition 63

In 2002, under the leadership of then Assembly member Darrell Steinberg and California Council for Community Mental Health Agencies Executive Director Rusty Selix, a grassroots movement throughout the State resulted in the signatures needed for an initiative on the November 4, 2004 ballot. Proposition 63 was created to reduce the long-term adverse impact of untreated mental illness through providing the kind of help people need when they need it.

The Act is designed to fully fund California's children's system of care program and California's adult and older adult system of care. By imposing a 1% surtax on personal incomes over $1 million, the Legislative Analyst and Department of Finance estimated that the funding increase would average $800 million over the first five years. In fact that estimate was exceeded from the start and the funds have constituted a 10 – 15% increase in overall mental health funding.

Mental Health Services Act:
Transformational Components, Promise and Challenges

Foundational Transformation

Proposition 63 became a law known as the Mental Health Services Act (MHSA) in January 2005. The Act did not increase funding for the old mental health system. Instead, it calls for complete transformation to a new system, based on the concepts and approach to treatment contained in nationally recognized documents, such as: The President's New Freedom Commission on Mental Health report, Crossing the Quality Chasm by the Institute of Medicine; and research by the Annapolis Coalition on the Workforce. The old law since Realignment in 1991 had a defined target population of only children with serious emotional disturbances and adults with severe mental illnesses. In contrast, the MHSA includes the prevention and early intervention dimension to keep mental illnesses from becoming so severe in the first place.

The MHSA was designed to transform from a "fail first" system of waiting for people to hit rock bottom to a "help first" norm in which everyone can receive the right care at the right time. Hospitalizations, incarcerations, out of home placements, special education and other "corrective" measures were previously the norm before getting needed services. Usually such conditions were endured for several years. The "help first" system dictates the following: that no child should "age

out" of the child welfare system and be dumped on the streets, that no one should be discharged from psychiatric hospitalization without follow up care or discharged from a jail or juvenile justice system without being enrolled in a program appropriate to their level of need. The concept of "supplantation" was introduced into the law to ensure that funds would not be used to maintain existing, underfunded programs. Implementation of these principles began slowly and carefully in 2005 and is still in process 5 years later. At the center of this transformation is a promise to be guided by the voices and preferences of the diverse communities of consumers and family members who rely on the local mental health systems.

Dr. Marvin J. Southard, Los Angeles County Department of Mental Health Director, has stated: "The most important change that the MHSA brought forward is to bring the voice of the person receiving services and the families across ethnicity to the center of the conversation rather than at the margins of the conversation."

Components of the MHSA

The Mental Health Services Act provides funding for the following services:

- Children's system of care, to be called Children's Community Services and Support
- Adult and older adult systems of care, to be called Adult and Older Adult Community Services and Support
- Prevention and early intervention
- Education and training programs to address the shortage of qualified mental health service providers
- Capital facilities and technology needed to provide mental health services

The Mental Health Services Act also requires that 5% of the funds for children's system of care, adult and older adult systems of care, and prevention and early intervention be used for innovative programs. Innovative programs include services that:

- Increase access for underserved groups
- Increase access to services
- Improve quality of services
- Promote interagency collaboration

MHSA: Vision and Promise

With the passage of Proposition 63, California became the first state to establish funding that could make the dream of a transformed public mental health system a reality. California subsequently captured the attention of health care providers and policy makers across the nation who followed with interest the implementation process. Harmonious visions of recovery were created by state-level leaders to serve as the foundation upon which principles, policies and rules would be developed.

The transformation requires the creation of a new culture. It requires an inclusive and collaborative approach to care that addresses the needs of the whole person and incorporates "whatever it takes" to provide adequate support. Recovery visions promote individual responsibility and competency through communicating respect and engaging consumers and family members actively in the process. Treatment planning is a joint process. Care is delivered when and where it is needed by a diversity of multiple service providers. Systems are seamless; support is comprehensive; and the spirit of hope, wellness and recovery is encompassing.

In promoting the implementation of this transformation, the California Department of Mental Health, State Quality Improvement Council presented the following Institute of Medicine Quality Chasm Principles and Rules for Behavioral Health:

Overarching Principles

» Care is provided in a way that promotes the self-defined recovery goals, family and child resiliency goals and the positive development of each person served.

» Care is provided in a culturally and linguistically competent way with sensitivity to and awareness of the person's self-identified culture, race, ethnicity, language preference, age, gender, sexual orientation, disability, religious/spiritual beliefs and socio-economic status.

» There are no disparities for individuals or groups of individuals in accessibility, availability or quality of mental health services provided.

Rules

» Care is based on continuous, effective, healing partnerships and respectful relationships. The mental health care system provides flexible access and is responsive at all times.

» Individualized care is based on the unique needs, values, and culture of the person and/or family served.

» The person and/or family served are informed and understand they are the source of control in their treatment.

» Persons served and those whom they may designate have the right to shared knowledge and the free flow of information.

» The best available evidence is used in each situation to create the best possible chance for achieving the desired outcomes as defined by the person and/or family served.

» Assuring the safety of persons and families served is a system priority at all times.

» All stakeholders in the mental health system have the knowledge to participate in both person/family-centered and systems-level decision-making.

» The mental health system anticipates and plans for individual, family and community needs.

» There is an ongoing and continuous effort to provide effective care and decrease waste of both system and person/family resources.

» There is cooperation across systems and among mental health providers to ensure the appropriate and timely exchange of information and coordination of effective care.

» Correcting current disparities in the behavioral health system is a critical step towards assuring timely equal access, utilization and quality of care to multicultural populations.

Incorporation of the principles and rules above entails breaking the rules by which our agencies and clinicians have lived for many years. It requires change, retraining, and learning new ways of existing in a treatment community. Accepting the vision requires a true revision of the perspectives that have provided guidance for how competent care is delivered. Transformation is a conceptual as well as a practical challenge.

Cultures and Challenges at the State Level

In its first five years the MHSA faced substantial challenges in relation to the reality of implementing this vision.

- A fragmented health care system, consisting of entities that functioned based on their own unique policies, protocol and structure were required to plan and work collaboratively. Worlds opened up and managers were displaced and sometimes

uncomfortable.

- Mandates for inclusive planning and development that involved all stakeholders slowed down and complicated the process.

- County autonomy was impacted by the levels of management, administration and oversight built into the implementation process.

- The "rules" for billing, documentation and the concept of supplantation needed to be created, learned and relearned.

- A "two tiered" system of care surfaced, in which the stunning contrast between care provided to consumers who were still in traditional programs and those involved in the "field-capable" and full-service partnership systems became an issue of concern.

- Funding exceeded the projected amounts and a "reserve" was built. This created impatience with the implementation process and resulted in an overall threat to the funds when some California legislators wanted to claim the reserves in order to help solve the state's budget deficit problems in 2009.

- As the transformation has moved forward, it has become evident that "whatever it takes" includes an encompassing reach into the community to pull in services such as primary care, education, employment and correctional programs in a co-located setting or with procedures and systems in place to provide for comfortable sharing of resources.

In addition to the "big picture" challenges addressed above, each individual work setting was faced with a paradigm shift and clinicians were often asked to change their perspectives, practices, attitudes and belief systems. This required culture change is critical for the transformation to succeed. Without a true buy-in of the managers, supervisors and clinicians, the whole transformation process remains at the level of concept and vision. If change is not implemented at the direct service level, it simply won't happen. At this more micro level, the issues have been equally as challenging as those that pertain to the big picture.

Cultures and Challenges: Paradigm Shift within the Treatment Settings

- Stigma is alive and well within the community settings and among service providers. Perceptions and attitudes about individuals who suffer from serious mental illness can inadvertently prevail in treatment as well as within working relationships.

- Previous images and expectations of professional status may not be upheld as the work of the clinician extends to diverse support services and the traditional "office"

treatment setting is no longer the norm.

- Working in a multidisciplinary setting as part of a team may create a shift in power that is disconcerting or confusing for the clinician. Prior training and supervision often did not prepare the clinician for a process of sharing the treatment responsibility and decision-making.

- The training of most clinicians was based on the medical model. Recovery-oriented care challenges traditional boundaries and ethics, leaving supervisors insecure about how and under what circumstances to adhere to these long-standing rules of conduct.

- Integration of consumers as peers may be uncomfortable for clinicians both in relation to the joint process of treatment planning and in the teamwork approach to care.

- Many clinicians who are now working in the public mental health system were not trained in the basic tenets of recovery-oriented care such as Evidenced Based Practice, cultural awareness, and co-occurring disorders. The balancing process of learning new methods for delivering care while comfortably integrating long standing treatment orientations can pose complicated challenges.

- Methods of documentation previously utilized in the public system must be revised to satisfy the traditional requirements for billing, yet reflect new treatment modalities and practice.

- Supervisors without previous training in recovery, hope and wellness oriented treatment must learn how to effectively guide interns who enter the system as providers.

Cultural change is difficult. Almost by definition culture encompasses the things we take for granted, that we assume have to be the way they've always been, that we pass on from generation to generation in so many ways. It's unreasonable to expect programs to change their cultures just because it would be more effective. There is much inertia and too much vested interest in the existing culture. In addition, the present infrastructure of our mental health system supports the traditional treatment culture, not the recovery culture. In numerous ways, from funding mechanisms to administrative priorities, from service fragmentation to staff hiring patterns, from training programs to paperwork requirements, recovery is systematically undermined. It requires intensive, intentional efforts to build recovery cultures. The true opportunity that the Mental Health Services Act gives us is the combination of funds to establish new programs along with a new infrastructure designed to promote recovery.

Current Shifts and Changes

California has been in a unique position, in that Proposition 63 secured funding for ongoing transformation efforts. With the passage of Healthcare Reform in 2010, advanced funds became available to provide the state with a "jumpstart" for implementation. California was one of the states granted 1115 Waiver funds in 2011, referred to as the "Bridge to Healthcare Reform."

With the 1115 Waiver funds and a newly elected Governor in place, major shifts and restructure have been implemented in the California public mental health system. Most notably, the California State Department of Mental Health is in the process of being dissolved, with oversight and management of the publicly funded MediCal services being shifted to the Department of Health Care Services. This shift establishes a structure of integrated services at the state level. MHSA funds, which will continue to supplement – but not supplant – traditional services, will still be monitored by the MHSA Oversight and Accountability Commission; however, a great deal of autonomy in relation to utilization of these funds will be given to the 58 counties throughout the state. Decisions will be made and funds will be designated at the county level.

This transformation is an ongoing and long-term process. Federal healthcare reform and developing comprehensive systems of accountable care will impact the future directions, structures and routes that guide California's process. However, the evolving national systems of healthcare reinforce and support the principles of the Mental Health Services Act and the implementation of recovery-oriented care, placing California on the leading edge going forward.

Discussion Questions:

1. What are your thoughts about the pros and cons of involving stakeholders in planning for mental health care in their communities?

2. Is it fair to tax millionaires in order to fund the transformation? Why?

3. Proposition 63 was designed to provide "whatever it takes" and to turn our treatment system into a "help first" instead of "fail first" response to those in need. Is it working? Why?

4. What is the best way to monitor the use of MHSA funds throughout the state? If you were in charge of the funds, how would you make decisions about distribution?

5. Why do you think Proposition 63 was passed by voters in California?

BRINGING IT HOME: COUNTY AND COMMUNITY RECOVERY-ORIENTED BEHAVIORAL HEALTHCARE: NOTES ON A PARADIGM CHANGE/CULTURE SHIFT

Mary M. Read, Ph.D.

Recovery is, according to one consumer, researcher, and author: "...a deeply personal, unique process of changing one's attitudes, values, feelings, goals, skills and/or roles. It is a way of living a satisfying, hopeful and contributing life even with limitations caused by illness. Recovery involves the development of new meaning and purpose in one's life as one grows beyond the catastrophic effects of mental illness." (Anthony, 1993, p. 15).

To another, recovery means the rebuilding of self and hope through learning responsibility and accountability (Deegan, 1996), while to a third author recovery is simply "saying yes to life" (Fisher, 1992, p. 5). A knowledge of what the recovery orientation to mental health care is, the societal forces from which it arose, its theoretical underpinnings and how it is currently being funded and implemented are essential for competent service delivery in today's milieu of supporting mental wellness for all. This section provides a brief overview of the cultural shift toward recovery and resilience as the dominant themes of healthcare delivery in the 21st century.

As described in the History of the Mental Health Services Act (MHSA) in California, prior to the 1960s, all people with severe (and/or persistent) mental illnesses (SMI or SPMI) were viewed as totally dependent on institutional care. The institution comprised the totality of treatment available, and seclusion from the rest of the populace was seen as both desirable and justified (Beale & Lambric, 1995). Since de-institutionalization alone did not automatically meet the needs of persons with SMI/SPMI ("consumers"), in the mid-1970s the National Institute of Mental Health (NIMH) created Community Support Systems (CSS) in an attempt to rectify unmet vocational, housing, educational, and social needs of consumers. The goal of the CSS was to develop "a network of caring and responsible people committed to assisting a vulnerable population meet their needs and develop their potentials without being unnecessarily isolated or excluded from the community" (Beale & Lambric, 1995, p. 6). This represents an early articulation of what became the 'recovery orientation' to healthcare, which was consistent with and grew out of the burgeoning Consumer Advocacy and Civil Rights movements of the 1960s and 70s.

The NIMH CSS federal guidelines were complementary with the philosophy of several states implementing a recovery orientation to healthcare into their mental health delivery services (e.g., Connecticut, Ohio, Wisconsin), partly as a response to the rise of managed care. For example,

the Ohio Department of Mental Health's (ODMH) philosophy was that "people with severe and persistent mental illness have the right to live in the community and participate in the lifestyle of their choice" (Beale & Lambric, 1995, p. 6). The ODMH Community Support Program's (CSP) philosophy statement posits: "...a comprehensive program utilizing state of the art psychiatric, vocational, housing, nursing and social services tailored to individual needs will benefit all persons with severe mental disability and, moreover, may result in a complete recovery for a substantial proportion of previously determined 'hopeless cases' " (Beale & Lambric, 1995, p. 6). The essential components needed to provide these services included: mental health treatment, case management, crisis response services, family and community support, peer support, rehabilitation services, self-help, housing, health and dental care, income support and entitlement, and protection and advocacy (Anthony, Cohen & Farcus, 1990). Further, the CSP noted that these components should: "be consumer centered, empower clients, be racially and culturally appropriate, be flexible, focus on strengths, be normalized and incorporate natural supports, and the service system should be accountable" (Beale & Lambric, 1995, p. 6).

By integrating the CSS guidelines (above) with the rehabilitation model put forward by Anthony et al., (1990), the hope was to move beyond a medical model of service delivery to incorporate a more holistic response to the difficulties faced by persons dealing with SMI. Anthony (1993), himself a consumer of mental health services for SMI, described the sequelae of SMI as encompassing **dysfunction** (e.g., lack of work and social skills), **disability** (e.g., homelessness and unemployment), and **disadvantage** (e.g., poverty and discrimination). Anthony et al., (1990) put forward nine basic principles of the rehabilitation model, most of which were then carried into the recovery orientation as it developed. These principles briefly include: a primary focus on improving competencies rather than simply alleviating pathology and symptoms, helping the consumer adjust to environmental requirements, using any and all effective techniques, focusing on improving vocational outcomes, hope as an essential ingredient, a belief that consumers can become more independent if suitable accommodations are made; the need for consumers to be actively involved in their rehabilitation plan, the development of client skills and community supports as the twin pillars of the model, and the recognition that while long-term medication support may be needed, as it is seldom sufficient in and of itself as a treatment for SMI.

Another definition of recovery from the early 1990's comes from Hatfield and Lefley (1993, p. 184): Recovery from a major mental illness does not usually mean a 'cure' or return to the pre-morbid state. Rather, it means a kind of re-adaptation to the illness that allows life to go forward in a meaningful way. The adaptive response is not an end state; it is a **process** in which the person is continually trying to maximize the fit between his or her needs and the environment. Such an adaptation (recovery) process requires cooperation and collaboration between consumers, their

communities, and the mental health professionals who aim to serve them. Recovery also requires an environment where consumers have access to three key elements: hope; a sense of control, responsibility or empowerment over their lives; and an acceptance of the illness, though not as the defining quality of their personhood. Anthony (1993, p. 18-20) adds several assumptions about recovery from SMI, including that it can occur without professional intervention, does not mean that mental illness was never present, can be present even if symptoms reoccur, changes the frequency and duration of symptoms, is not a function of one's theory about the causes of SMI, requires people who believe in and stand by the person in need of recovery, is not (and does not feel like) a linear process, and that recovery from the (social, financial, physical, emotional, etc.) **consequences** of SMI is sometimes more difficult than recovery from the SMI itself. Such tenets are inherently systemic in their view recursively connecting the consumer to his/her nested environmental contexts.

While the President's New Freedom Commission (2003) "strongly urged the adoption of the notion of recovery as possible for all and as the guiding vision for the system" (Farkas, 2007, p. 68), from the variety of definitions attributed to the recovery orientation/model/process, it is clear that, whatever 'recovery' is, it is a polyvalent concept (Pilgrim, 2008). Gaining a clear understanding of this broad (and still somewhat contested) guiding principle for healthcare is essential for the competent delivery of mental health services. Different groups creating rubrics for understanding recovery during the early 1990s developed lists of themes to illuminate the process quality of the phenomenon under discussion. As an exemplar, the ODMH CSP Advisory Committee highlighted eight major themes that are fairly representative of these groups (Beale & Lambric, 1995, p. 9):

1. Meaningful employment positively impacts the recovery process.
2. Stigma re: SMI continues to be a major barrier to the recovery process.
3. Positive human relationships can lay the foundation for recovery.
4. Consumers' desire to develop positive, collaborative relationships with service providers.
5. Peer support is a definite aid to recovery.
6. Consumers want more control over their lives.
7. Education contributes to one's recovery, and
8. Having access to needed resources improves the likelihood of recovery.

Other states were also changing the way they configured mental health care and embracing the recovery orientation. For example, according to researchers in Wisconsin:

Recovery refers to both internal conditions experienced by persons who describe themselves as being in recovery--hope, healing, empowerment and connection-- and external conditions that facilitate recovery -- implementation of the principle of human rights, a positive culture of healing, and recovery-oriented services (Jacobson & Greenley, 2001, p. 482).

In the 1990s, states faced a reconfiguration of healthcare delivery systems due to the influence and constraints of managed care. 'Recovery' became a watchword during this process, guiding the reform of both policy and practice. Changing from an institutionalized model of care for SMI to a client-centered, community-based, consumer-driven, collaborative and empowering recovery vision naturally required a concomitant shift in funding priorities, service delivery models, theoretical underpinnings and research techniques. The paradigm shift included moving beyond a focus on pathology and professionally directed treatments to observing and embracing the lived experience of consumers' recovery processes, while offering support and encouragement as they rebuilt/reclaimed their lives (Davidson & White, 2007). Since even 'mental' health or illness as a construct may be stigmatizing to healthcare consumers, the term 'behavioral' healthcare is often used in describing the recovery orientation, since the behavioral signs of SMI are visible, while the 'mental' ones are more abstract and dependent on theory. This distinction can be important, as it helps shape the family and community response to the consumer dealing with the SMI. As Sullivan (1994, p. 11) notes, "How families understand mental illness, and the nature of professional help offered them, shapes the caregiving process."

A major drive borne of the Consumer movement (whose slogan was "Nothing about us without us!") is the incorporation of consumers at every level of policy, planning, training, delivery, and evaluation of mental health services. Another drive toward recovery came from the Independent Living Movement for persons with physical disabilities (Deegan, 1992) which spearheaded the passage of the Americans with Disabilities Act for employment fairness and community/housing inclusion. These drives impact the delivery of recovery-oriented care, in that collaboration and cooperation with the larger community and consumers in recovery, not just one's clients, supervisors/supervisees and colleagues, is required to participate fully in a 'recovery vision'. Ensuring clients' housing and employment needs are met also becomes part of the 'wraparound services' necessary to implement and sustain consumers' recovery visions.

According to the Board of Behavioral Sciences (BBS) in California, the focus of Recovery-oriented Healthcare is resilience, including the personal and community qualities that enable persons to cope with adversity, trauma, tragedy, threats, or other stresses. Recovery-oriented mental healthcare incorporates some changes in basic tenets away from a medical model of treatment, including the following:

1. Mental illness no longer considered a life sentence.

2. The provider is now viewed as a partner in care, not as directing treatment.

3. The treatment goal is to help consumers develop meaningful roles in their communities, not to develop a long-term therapeutic relationship with the therapist.

4. Consumers play a more active role in decision-making and taking responsibility for their own recovery.

5. Delivering in-vivo care became the ideal, vs. treatment rendered within the mental health center.

6. The importance of support systems, including family, peers and community members, became more and more central to attaining and maintaining recovery (Berger, 2004).

Retrieved from http://www.bbs.ca.gov/pdf/mhsa/resource/recovery/practice_change.pdf

There is some debate (e.g., Torrey & Wyzik, 2000) about the concept of recovery being too vague or poorly defined to be useful, and potentially too optimistic for the level of severity and chronicity that can be involved in the course of a SPMI. Concerns are raised as to whether 'recovery' applies only to consumers with less severe symptoms or greater access to community resources (also termed recovery capital, Granfield & Cloud, 1999), potentially causing a 'blame the victim' scenario (albeit inadvertently) for those more adversely affected and/or less able to connect to resources. As more qualitative research has emerged detailing narratives of consumers' journeys of recovery (e.g., Davidson, 2003; Deegan, 1996; Leibrich, 1999), these concerns have diminished somewhat. However, Dickerson (2006) points out that the problems of poverty and lack of access to healthcare are not specifically remedied by the 'recovery orientation'.

Since 'recovery' is not synonymous with 'cure', it may be more useful to connect it to the concept of 'healing', which implies both a sense of control (e.g., managing one's symptoms, having an internal locus of control) and the ability to define one's self apart from/beyond the illness (Jacobson & Greenley, 2001). Davidson and Roe (2007) make a useful distinction between the sense of 'recovery from' an illness (with complete symptom remission and an exit from the role of patient) and 'recovery in' a situation, similar to the use of 'recovery' in Alcoholics Anonymous. For the latter sense of recovery to be operative, consumers recognize that SMI is a condition to be lived with daily, make progress about when possible (especially by making use of community and peer supports), and learn to make meaning of their lives around, even as symptoms may return or fluctuate in severity. As Pilgrim (2008) notes, this distinction moves 'recovery' away from statistical and diagnostic analysis (recovery from) to a more social and existential analysis (recovery in).

This shift in philosophy mirrors the move in healthcare from the biomedical model as the only relevant determinant of care, to the middle ground of community-oriented healthcare (more inclusive but not yet as radical as consumer-driven recovery) and on to the present scenario of 'psychiatric survivors' who become experts by their own experiences and reject the authority of healthcare professionals to define for them what their recovery is and how to reach it. So the emphasis in recovery is dependent on what is being recovered from (or in) -- an illness, with an outcome of successful treatment; an impairment, with rehabilitation as the goal; or invalidation (through stigma, disempowerment, etc.) with surviving and even thriving as the hope-full recovery goal (Pilgrim, 2008). The latter focuses on consumers' lived experiences, shying away from the 'power over' potentials of involuntary restraint, diagnoses as lifelong labels, and social exclusion. These tensions are by no means resolved; rather, they continue as undercurrents within which the political and monetary forces behind healthcare reform as well as the social justice movements advocated by consumers continually move. And, as Smith-Merry, Freeman & Sturdy (2011) note:

Recovery is generally defined in terms of the kinds of values that should pervade the provision of mental health care, and the way that service providers and users conceive of their respective roles and relationships. But that definition says little about how such values and changes in role can best be achieved in practice" (p. 22).

Hence the need for multi-modal research and thoughtful critique as the practices of wellness and recovery are expanded.

It is important to note that whenever consumers with SMI/SPMI are included more fully in their community environments, the specter of risk to those communities is also present in the mix (Pilgrim, 2008). Students, professionals-in-training and staff with whom consumers will interact may harbor some of these fears, and/or privately held biases about persons who are experiencing or have experienced SMI/SPMI. Working to dispel prejudice while adequately managing risk factors is a tension that clinicians will have to bridge effectively with their colleagues and clients.

In focusing on hope and consumer empowerment/responsibilities, care must also be taken not to lose sight of society's duty to become more tolerant of diversity, less stigmatizing of the 'differently-abled', and committed to funding adequate resources for all its members, to bring about the solution-saturated context that full access to recovery requires. Otherwise, the shift to counting persons who live in communities and manage their symptoms as 'recovered' could become the harbinger of funding cuts and program closures, rather than the opposite (Oyebode, 2004). A true 'recovery orientation' is not about reducing resources, but focuses on mobilizing resourcefulness (Roberts & Hollins, 2007), which is both a sustainable and socially just endeavor. In evaluating a consumer's recovery

capital -- defined by Granfield and Cloud (1999) as the internal and external assets one can draw to initiate and sustain recovery, while achieving a meaningful life in the community of one's choosing -- recovery-oriented healthcare integrates cultural renewal and community development efforts in order to foster greater access to such resources. This helps avoid labeling the client as 'less than' or at fault for any perceived lack of recovery capital. Instead, recovery-oriented healthcare providers/ partners take into account society's role in the amount of resources allocated toward recovery while working toward (and holding hope and optimism for) the creation of more resources, benefitting all of society.

Participating in supervision and service delivery in the (continually evolving) recovery orientation naturally requires learning new skills along the way. Training clinicians is essential in order to foster these new skills, and eventually shift the 'clinical culture' into the collaborative, respectful, consumer-driven, 'doing whatever it takes' practicality of recovery in the 21st century. For instance, instead of anticipating a lifelong, debilitating course of illness, clinicians will speak in hopeful ways about multiple pathways of recovery. Instead of viewing increasing stress as something from which the client may need to be protected, the recovery-oriented clinician will encourage and coach the consumer to embrace and manage life stresses. Supporting healthy risk-taking (rather than shielding clients from risk by making decisions for them) can help encourage and motivate consumers to grow, reinforcing their strengths (Torrey & Wyzik, 2000). The concept of 'transcendent recovery' (Davidson & White, 2007), represents a heightened functional level (both personal and interpersonal) achieved through facing and overcoming the limitations imposed by severe, complex disorders like SMI. This transcendent aspect implies not just a return to former functioning (as in the old definition of recovery), but a value-added recognition for having taken what Life brought and making the best of it, and themselves. To help support this type of recovery vision, recovery-oriented clinicians continually re-focus their attention on client strengths, pathways of support, and ways to re-engage and encourage their clients (White & Kurtz, 2006), as well as conducting research that privileges the perspective of consumers (Resnick & Rosenheck, 2008).

Service planning is another recovery dimension to consider in the recovery orientation to mental wellness (Felton, Cashin, & Brown, 2010). The quality improvement brought about by implementing a recovery orientation arises from increased collaboration with consumers and their systemic environments. As Torrey and Wyzik (2000) note:

> Consumers cannot meaningfully direct their own mental health services if the
> planning process is too complicated to understand. Educational materials that
> explain the service planning process, service plans that are written in accessible,
> non-clinical language, and an open planning process that gives ample time to

think through life goals all enhance consumer's ability to take charge of their
mental health care. (p. 213)

Empowering clients by fostering their sense of agency must be tempered with the knowledge
that society is not necessarily structured or prepared to embrace their 'recovery visions' as actual
action plans.

While working to implement mental wellness plans, it is important to remain aware of the differing
political agendas (e.g., funding cuts/priorities, risk management, social inclusion/ mainstreaming)
that influence how recovery is implemented, as well as what it means. As Dickerson (2006) warns,
SMI can be very disabling, and our science has not yet produced a cure nor been effective with
prevention; just learning to live better in the face of mental illness does not change those facts.
Nevertheless, recovery is the way of healthcare at this time (Ramon et. al., 2009), so understanding
(and critiquing) it is essential to providing competent mental (or 'behavioral') healthcare in the future.
According to Aarons et al., (2009) the movement toward evidence-based practice requires service
providers to blend these new skills with their own clinical expertise, in the context of a relationship
with consumers based on shared decision-making and choice. Michael A. Mancini (2011) notes
that utilizing collaborative research approaches, giving voice to consumers, academics, public policy
makers and local communities, is essential in helping the promise of the recovery orientation come
to fruition. He suggests employing critical discourse analysis within a participatory action research
framework as a way to foster such collaboration, while also maintaining a critique of recovery-
oriented policies in a socially just way.

Many of the concepts associated with the recovery orientation are inherently existential,
focusing on choice, responsibility, freedom, and meaning-making as essential human pursuits.
Any of the counseling theories that draw on this philosophy as a base (e.g., narrative, feminist,
humanistic) could be appropriate to use as a guiding framework for working with clients. As well,
motivation is a key ingredient in the recovery orientation -- motivation of the client, the caregivers
and community supporters, and the clinicians. Expanding our vision to include all of society, with
consumers inclusively embraced and supported, will mean adapting service plans to include aspects
that survivors of SMIs count as primarily important, even when these are non-traditional, under-
researched areas. These areas include but are not limited to spirituality, creativity and the arts, self-
management, gardening and other hobbies, pets, satisfactory work, adequate housing and finances,
and peer support (Leibrich, 1999). According to Torrey and Wyzik (2000, p. 215), "Operationalizing
the recovery vision requires bridging concepts. The bridges are supplied by consumer accounts
of their life journeys which portray recovery as a shift out of hopelessness, powerlessness, and an
illness-dominated sense of self." These existential ideals match the constructs coming out of consumer

narratives, where the focus is not on achieving some mental health professional's definition of 'normal life', but on embracing the SMI survivor's vocation of becoming more deeply, fully human (Deegan, 1996). The development of new purpose and meaningfulness in life, beyond the impact of mental illness, is a central outcome of the hope inherent in recovery (Anthony, 1993).

Meeting consumers where they are in their lives helps foster their intrinsic motivation to grow and thrive. Ensuring that a positive culture of healing exists within which the client's motivation can flourish, "begins with an environment characterized by tolerance, listening, empathy, compassion, respect, safety, trust, diversity, and cultural competence...oriented toward human rights for all individuals and groups" (Jacobson & Greenley, 2001, p. 484). Recovery-oriented clinicians need to be aware that the development of collaborative relationships between all parties -- consumers, providers, family and community supporters/caregivers -- is foundational to such a positive culture of healing. In the recovery orientation, such collaboration focuses on the consumer's choices, even when these differ from the choices the clinician or supervisor would have selected for them. According to Jacobson and Curtis (2000), issues that help support such a culture include dignity and respect, challenging stigma and discrimination, reflective practice and continuous improvement, empowerment and personal responsibility, cultural sensitivity and safety, spirituality and personal meaning, and consumer and family involvement. The involvement of consumer/peer providers hired by mental health agencies is part of alleviating stigma and sharing hope. Defined by SAMHSA as persons who are hired because they have/had a mental health condition and a history of involvement in the mental health system, the primary tasks for consumer/peer providers involve improving the client's utilization of services to promote full community integration.

Self-determination theory provides one framework for understanding the recovery orientation (Mancini, 2008; Ryan & Deci, 2000), as well as the process of transformed supervision within that orientation. Being both well researched and empirically-supported, this theory of human need fulfillment offers some attractive possibilities for deepening our understanding of recovery. Given that a loss of personal autonomy is a secondary consequence of SMI for nearly all consumers, a theory that explores the need for autonomy as foundational for human growth and happiness helps show why its loss or injury is so devastating. In this theory there are three basic human needs -- autonomy, relatedness to others, and competence -- the satisfaction of which are seen as foundational to well being and motivation and therefore essential elements of recovery. Mancini (2008), building on the work of Ryan and Deci (2000), posits that reinforcing a sense of autonomy is the pivotal basis of recovery-oriented healthcare. Autonomy heavily influences motivation, critical to positive healthcare outcomes, and is likely to be eroded during the stressful course of a SMI. According to Farkas (2007), outcome research indicates that having a meaningful, collaborative involvement in the planning and delivery of services increases a sense of empowerment, motivation, and shift in

identity (away from passive patient/victim to survivor and meaning-maker) through an increased sense of autonomy. Indeed, she labels self-choice/self-determination "the cornerstone of a recovery process." (Farkas, p. 71)

Both internal motivation (seeking novelty and challenge) and external motivation (seeking to gain reward or avoid sanction) are important to the satisfaction of the need for autonomy in self-determination theory. Within external motivation a distinction is drawn between degrees of personal choice, highlighting the need for as much autonomy as possible. "For example, a person with serious mental illness may take medication purely to comply with external pressures and contingencies or may take it out of a genuine belief that it is beneficial and will help them achieve other goals" (Mancini, 2008, p. 360). Both are external motivations, though the latter embraces more choice and agency for the consumer (e.g., Deegan & Drake, 2006). Mead and Copeland (2000) note that people who have been receiving mental health services for many years often develop a way of seeing themselves and relating to mental health professionals that reinforces their 'patient' identity, but does not expand their autonomy, unless the professional intentionally and consciously helps change the context. Supporting consumers to make leaps of faith, take risks that are self-defined (not prescribed by another) and redefine for themselves who they'd like to become in the process of their recovery from SMI helps uncover internal resources in the client that may have been buried under layers of stigma and imposed limitations.

Self-agency and choice are repeated themes in recovery literature, attesting the importance of autonomy. The second drive in self-determination theory -- the need for competence-- is also reflected in recovery themes, especially related to desires for meaningful work and lessening stigma. The centrality of community involvement and integration, peer support, and sharing 'experience, strength and hope' with other SMI survivors reflect the need for connectedness, the third pillar of self-determination theory. This latter emphasis may render the theory especially useful to conceptualize recovery when serving consumers whose level of disability and/or risk has generated a need for higher levels of service (Abbott, 2008).

Overall, the language of recovery is one of hope and high expectation. As well, the modeling of these attitudes can help produce them in others, from clinician to consumer, or from supervisor to clinician, through the phenomenon of parallel process (Doehrman, 1976). Sustaining one's own hope and morale is therefore another key 'recovery competency' as noted by Roberts and Hollins (2007). Since community is seen as the ultimate healing agent, not treatment (White & Kurtz, 2006), working to empower and encourage whole communities is also the work of recovery-oriented mental health. Success in recovery-focused service provision is then measured by short- and long-range improvements in individuals, their families/circles of care, and their surrounding communities.

Examples of short-term individual and family outcomes include early identification, bio-psychosocial stabilization, and assertive linkage to recovery communities. Identification of recovery support resources and fostering linkage between treatment providers and indigenous communities of recovery are some community short-term outcomes. Likewise, long-term family and individual outcomes focus on the improvement of global health and functioning, along with the sustained reduction and/or resolution of mental health problems, while community long-term outcomes include expanding the physical/psychological/social spaces where recovery can flourish, and reducing stigma (White & Kurtz, 2006). Client-generated recovery plans (as opposed to clinician-generated treatment plans), help broaden the focus of clinical work to include these larger domains and incorporate sometimes-neglected aspects such as spirituality, advocacy, and political action to influence funding and regulations (Borkman, 1997).

For example, SAMHSA has developed an ADS Resource Center, to promote **A**cceptance, **D**ignity, and **S**ocial Inclusion associated with Mental Health, including increased understanding of "intense spiritual experiences" (http://www.promoteacceptance.samhsa.gov). In their view, "mental health programs should educate staff about intense spiritual experiences, how best to support a person having one and how to distinguish between an intense spiritual experience that they can safely accompany someone through as opposed to one that requires intervention or even hospitalization" (Mancuso, 2011). Resources such as these, incorporating the lived experience of consumers with the research and expertise of a broad spectrum of healthcare providers and advocates, demonstrates the recovery orientation even as it helps to prepare the next generation of clinicians.

To facilitate consumer's resilience, clinicians working in the recovery orientation help model and support hope for their clients, supervisors/supervisees, staff, and community support networks. Solution-focused language (e.g., O'Hanlon & Weiner-Davis, 1988) can help consumers envision a desired future toward which clinicians can support their movement. Using clinical supervision as a practice ground for this hopeful envisioning with solution-saturated language is part of the best-practices approach embraced in the recovery orientation. At times, consumers may feel too hopeless (from the ravages of the SMI and/or society's response to it) to embrace this positive language and vision. Linehan's (1993) suggestions for helping discouraged clients may be useful in such cases. These include having clinicians balance an unfailing belief in the consumer's potential for change with a radical acceptance of their current circumstances, while communicating both of these clearly and consistently. It is also important to remember that the 'resistant' or 'apathetic' client may be struggling to cope with very severe symptoms, discouragement or hopelessness, personality type, lack of accessible information regarding options/choices, and a 'Catch 22' about maintaining the status quo to continue on mental health disability benefits while attempting to recover from SMI (Mead & Copeland, 2000).

In the recovery movement, consumers speak for themselves. From these narrative accounts, clinicians and supervisors may draw many helpful pointers as to how to proceed in the transformation process as a service provider. For example, Shery Mead and Mary Ellen Copeland (2000), themselves both consumers and mental health professionals, point out that:

> A truly supportive therapeutic relationship begins with honesty and a willingness to take a critical look at assumptions learned during training. Clinical support, in a recovery environment, means at the same time that clinicians attempt to take care of a person, they also hold the person accountable for his or her behavior and believe in the ability to change. (p. 320)

They also pose several questions that health care professionals can use to guide their development in service provision under a recovery rubric (Mead & Copeland, 2000):

- How much of our own discomfort are we willing to sit with while someone is trying out new choices?

- How are our boundaries continuously being redefined as we struggle to deepen each individual relationship?

- What are the assumptions we have about this person, by virtue of his/her diagnosis, history, and lifestyle? How can we put aside our assumptions and predictions in order to be fully present to the situation and open to the possibility for the other person to do the same?

- What are the barriers that might prevent both of us from stretching and growing? (p. 320)

More research and better longitudinal studies are clearly needed in the developing field of recovery-oriented mental healthcare. What is clear from research to date is that "recovery" is possible over time; represents a multidimensional, highly individualized non-linear process that can be described; may be achieved with or without professional intervention; [and] has multiple objective and subjective outcome indicators that reach beyond symptom reduction" (Farkas, 2007, p. 70). Farkas holds that reflecting at least the four core recovery values present in the literature (person involvement, person orientation, growth potential, and self-determination/choice) will help clinicians and other service providers operate from an evidence base to remain effective and relevant in the lives of those they serve. Becoming a recovery-oriented clinician (and it is a continual process of becoming, like any existential endeavor) involves consuming and even generating recovery-oriented research, so that all of society may benefit from the insights and interactions of people committed to mental wellness.

References

Aarons, G., Wells, R. S., Zagursky, K., Fettes, D. & Palinkas, L. A. (2009). Implementing evidence-based practice in community mental health agencies: A multiple stakeholder analysis. *American Journal of Public Health, 99*(11), pp. 2087–95.

Abbott, P. (2008). Another step toward understanding recovery? *Advances in Psychiatric Treatment, 14,* 366-368.

American Psychiatric Association (2005). Position statment: Use of the concept of recovery. Retrieved from http://www.psychiatry.org/advocacy--newsroom/position-statements

Anthony, W.A. (1993). Recovery from mental illness: The guiding vision of the mental health service system in the 1990s. *Psychosocial Rehabilitation Journal, 16,* 11-23.

Anthony, W.A., Cohen, M.R., & Farcus, M.D. (1990). *Psychiatric rehabilitation.* Boston University: Boston, MA.

Beale, V. & Lambric, T. (1995). *The recovery concept: Implementation in the mental health system. A report by the Community Support Program Advisory Committee.* Columbus: Ohio Department of Mental Health.

Borkman, T. (1997). Is recovery planning any different than treatment planning? *Journal of Substance Abuse Treatment, 15*(1), 37-42.

Davidson, L. (2003). *Living outside mental illness: Qualitative studies of recovery in schizophrenia.* New York University Press.

Davidson, L., & Roe, D. (2007). 'Recovery from' and 'recovery in' serious mental illness: One strategy for lessening confusion plaguing recovery. *Journal of Mental Health, 16*(4), 459-70.

Davidson, L., & White, W. (2007). The concept of recovery as an organizing principle for integrating mental health services and addiction services. *Journal of Behavioral Health Services and Research, 34*(2), 109-120.

Deegan, P. E. (1996). Recovery as a journey of the heart. *Psychosocial Rehabilitation Journal, 19*(3), 91-97.

Deegan, P. E. and Drake, R. E. (2006). Shared decision-making and medication management in the recovery process: From compliance to alliance. *Psychiatric Services, 57(11),* 1636–1639.

Dickerson, F.B. (2006). Disquieting aspects of the recovery paradigm. *Psychiatric Services, 57(5)*. 647.

Doehrman, M.J. (1976). P*arallel process in supervision and psychotherapy. Bulletin of the Menninger Clinic, 40,* 1-104.

Farkas, M. (2007). The vision of recovery today: What it is and what it means for services. *World Psychiatry, 6,* 68-74.

Felton, M. C., Cashin, C. E., & Brown, T. T. (2010). What does it take? California county funding requests for recovery-oriented full service partnerships under the Mental Health Services Act. *Community Mental Health Journal, 46*(5), 441-451. doi:10.1007/s10597-010-9304-6

Fisher, D.B. (1992). Humanizing the recovery process. Resources, 4, 5-6. Granfield, R., & Cloud, W. (1999). *Coming clean: Overcoming addiction without treatment.* New York: New York University Press.

Jacobson, N. & Curtis L.C. (2000). Recovery as a policy in mental health services: strategies emerging from the states. *Psychiatric Rehabilitation Journal 23*(4), 333-341.

Jacobson, N., & Greenley, D. (2001). What is recovery? A conceptual model and explication. *Psychiatric Services, 52*(4), 482-485.

Leibrich, J. (1999). *A gift of stories: Discovering how to deal with mental illness.* University of Chicago Press.

Linehan, M. (1993). *Cognitive behavioral treatment of borderline personality disorder.* Guilford: New York.

Mancini, A.D. (2008). Self-determination theory: A framework for the recovery paradigm. *Advances in Psychiatric Treatment, 14,* 358-365.

Mancini, M. A. (2011). Understanding change in community mental health practices through critical discourse analysis. *British Journal of Social Work 41,* 645–667. doi:10.1093/bjsw/bcr067

Mancuso, L. (2011). Multicultural competence, intense spiritual experiences, and mental health: A self-help, peer support and service provider technical assistance tool. Retrieved from http://www.scribd.com/doc/80470129/Mental-Health-Intense-Spiritual-Experiences

Mead, S., & Copeland, M.E. (2000). What recovery means to us: Consumer's perspectives. *Community Mental Health Journal, 36*(3), 315-328.

New Freedom Commission on Mental Health (2003). *Achieving the promise: Transforming mental health care in America. Final Report.* Rockville, MD: US Department of Health & Human Services.

O'Hanlon, W., & Weiner-Davis, M. (1988). *In search of solutions: Creating a context for change.* Norton: New York.

Onken, S.J., Craig, C.M., Ridgway, P., Ralph, R.O., & Cook, F.A. (2007). An analysis of the definitions and elements of recovery: A review of the literature. *Psychiatric Rehabilitation Journal, 31*(1), 9–22.

Oyebode, F. (2004). Invited commentary on: The rediscovery of recovery. *Advances in Psychiatric Treatment, 10,* 48-49.

Pilgrim, D. (2008). 'Recovery' and current mental health policy. *Chronic Illness, 4,* 295-304.

Ramon, S., Shera, W., Healy, B., Lachman, M., & Renouf, N. (2009). The rediscovered concept of recovery in mental illness: A multicountry comparison of policy and practice. *International Journal of Mental Health, 38*(2), 106-126.

Resnick, S. G., & Rosenheck, R. A. (2008). Integrating peer-provided services: A quasi-experimental study of recovery orientation, confidence, and empowerment. *Psychiatric Services, 59*(11), 1307–1314.

Roberts, G., & Hollins, S. (2007). Recovery: Our common purpose? *Advances in Psychiatric Treatment, 13,* 397-99.

Ryan, R.M., & Deci, E.L. (2000). Self-determination theory and the facilitation of intrinsic motivation, social development, and well-being. *American Psychologist, 55,* 68-78.

Sullivan, P. (1994). Recovery from schizophrenia: What we can learn from the developing nations. *Innovations & Research in Clinical Services, Community Support and Rehabilitation, 3(2),* 7-15.

Torrey, W.C., & Wyzik, P. (2000). The recovery vision as a service improvement guide for community mental health center providers. *Community Mental Health Journal, 38*(2): 209-216.

White, W., & Kurtz, E. (2006). *Linking addiction treatment and communities of recovery: A primer for addiction counselors and recovery coaches.* Pittsburgh, PA: IRETA/NeATTC.

Discussion Questions:

1. Name some qualities associated with the recovery orientation to wellness. How do these qualities support a holistic sense of wellness? What other qualities do you think might be important for wellness?

2. The Consumer Movement was one of the social justice themes arising out of the 1960's and 70's – "Nothing About Us, Without Us." How might implementing recovery-oriented principles in mental health care help bring about more socially just outcomes for consumers? What strategies to involve consumers at every level – planning, policy, service delivery, evaluation, etc. – do you think could work in your local communities?

3. In the recovery orientation, the consumer is seen as the expert on their own life, yet you are getting extensive training to develop mental health expertise. How might this lack of 'expert status' affect you in your professional identity? How might it affect your supervisor, or the staff at your practicum/fieldwork placement?

4. A criticism that has been directed toward the recovery orientation is that it will lead to funding cuts for mental wellness/behavioral healthcare, since everyone can 'recover' from serious mental illness. What aspects (or principles) of the RO do you think will be needed to support continued consumer and community wellness?

5. Counseling requires a constant monitoring of the risk-to-benefit ratio for any behavior (e.g., feeling better from talking about problems vs. feeling worse for focusing on problems). Implementing the recovery orientation requires consumer's involvement and immersion in the community of their choice, which can increase that community's level of risk. What benefits do you see from an inclusive, community-based support model for mental wellness? What potential drawbacks do you envision?

PART TWO

ENTER THE CLINICIAN

- A Strengths-Based, Postmodern Approach to Recovery-Oriented Therapy with Persons Diagnosed with Severe Mental Illness

- Public System Practical Guidelines for Case Conceptualization in Recovery-oriented Care

- Public System Practical Guidelines for Treatment Planning and Documentation

- Boundaries and Ethical Considerations

- The Parallel Process

A STRENGTHS-BASED, POSTMODERN APPROACH TO RECOVERY-ORIENTED THERAPY WITH PERSONS DIAGNOSED WITH SEVERE MENTAL ILLNESS

Dana J. Stone, Ph.D. & Diane R. Gehart, Ph.D.

A key factor in the mental health recovery movement is working in a collaborative and appreciative manner with consumers. This chapter outlines how therapists can use elements of postmodern therapies—collaborative, narrative, and solution-focused—to work with individuals diagnosed with severe mental illness from a recovery perspective (Gehart, 2011a, 2011b). This approach draws upon theoretical constructs and practices with which most therapists are already familiar, allowing them to effectively work in newer recovery-oriented treatment contexts. The philosophical, political, and theoretical foundations of this approach are described elsewhere (Gehart, 2011a, 2011b); this chapter will highlight clinical applications.

With a collaborative and appreciative approach, the voices of consumers are honored and equally valued in the process of recovery (Anderson & Goolishian, 1992; Anderson, 1997; Gehart, 2011b). The most critical aspect of recovery-oriented treatment is the practitioner's ability to establish a working collaborative relationship with the consumer (Gehart, 2011b). Working with consumers using an appreciative approach draws on and integrates the strengths and abilities of the consumer throughout the recovery process.

While this model is a strengths-based approach, it is not for the faint of heart. The recovery oriented approach for working with the severely mentally ill is not easy, straightforward, painless, or without drama. The recovery oriented approach requires the practitioner to maintain hope and positive vision for their client's future when facing the numerous and painful obstacles throughout the journey of recovery. The collaborative, appreciative postmodern approach to conceptualizing recovery oriented treatment includes the following topics, which we will discuss in detail in this chapter:

- Establishing a recovery partnership
- Mapping the landscape of recovery
  - » Mapping a person's sense of life purpose
  - » Mapping a person's sense of belonging and intimacy
  - » Mapping a person's sense of hope
  - » Mapping a person's strengths and resources
  - » Mapping a person's mental health history
- Recovery treatment planning
- Recovery-oriented interventions
- Ethical implications of recovery-oriented practice

Recovery Partnership

It is useful for the practitioner in recovery-oriented work to think of him or her self as a supportive partner in the recovery process (Adams & Grieder, 2005). Unlike many models of therapy, the therapist in the recovery model joins with the client on their journey of recovery, rather than assuming the role of expert or change agent (Gehart, 2011b). The therapist in this role really holds safe and uninterrupted space for the consumer to share their ideas, their story, and their experiences living with a diagnosis. In order for a practitioner to be successful with a client in the recovery partnership and process, the therapist must demonstrate unwavering hope, maintain positive and genuine human connection, and be able to focus on the strengths of the client in the most difficult clinical circumstances. The therapist must believe that recovery is possible. Additionally, there is a significant aspect of this work that requires the therapist to recognize they are taking part in a unique and highly personal journey with another human being; suggesting a more personal commitment on the part of the therapist.

Mapping the Landscape of Recovery: Case Conceptualization

Mapping the landscape of recovery requires that the clinician, again, believe that recovery is possible. Mapping is a form of assessment that involves evaluating the consumer's mental status and diagnosis as well as the consumer's sense of purpose, sense of belonging, sense of hope, strengths and resources, and mental health status.

Mapping a Person's Sense of Purpose

Recovery from severe mental illness requires a compelling vision. Thus, the therapist's first task (after stabilizing crisis) is to help a consumer identify a sense of life purpose. To do so, clinicians often have to spend time helping consumers either reconnect with past dreams or help them identify new sources of life meaning (Davidson, Tondora, O'Connell, Lawless, & Rowe, 2009). Narrative and solution-focused questioning techniques are especially useful to identify and clarify a person's sense of purpose (Bertoline & O'Hanlon, 2002; De Jong & Berg, 2002; White, 2007; White & Epston, 1990). Examples of such future focused or presupposition questions will allow the therapist to focus with the client on when recovery will happen (O'Hanlon & Martin, 1992).

Questions for Mapping Sense of Purpose and Meaning

- What would you be doing with your life if your problems were completely resolved?

- What would you being doing if [diagnosis] was not keeping you from it?

- Before your symptoms became a problem, what did you enjoy most in your life? How will you know when you are ready to get back to it?

- When the problems caused by your [diagnosis] are gone, what will you be doing?

- Is there anything you have learned by having these symptoms that has helped you in any way? (Gehart, 2011b, p. 4)

Areas to discuss while mapping a person's sense of purpose may include employment and spirituality and religion. Employment is often a critical source for meaning and sense of purpose (Eklund, Hansson, & Ahlqvist, 2004), and consumers are encouraged to incorporate supported employment, volunteering, or other options for returning to work as soon as possible in the recovery process. Additionally, consumers may report spirituality and religious practices as helpful for finding meaning in their suffering. Supporting consumers in pursuing communities of support through religious affiliations may lead to feelings of warmth and acceptance for the consumer, which may also contribute to their feelings of belongingness.

Mapping a Sense of Belonging

Community is highly correlated with recovery and a sense of well-being (Gehart, 2011b). It is critical that therapists work with consumers to identify sources of belonging and intimacy such as family, friends, religious organizations, or support groups early in the recovery process. In cases where the consumer does not have a strong support system, it is necessary for the therapist to pay special attention in helping the consumer to build one. Examples of questions for mapping the consumer's connection to a community follow.

Questions for Mapping Connection and Intimacy

- From whom or where does your most meaningful social support or sense of connection come?

- Are there relationships that can be nurtured or repaired to increase you sense of feeling cared for or connected?

- Where do you feel you fit in the best? Now? In the past? What is it about these contexts that make you feel comfortable?

- To whom do you think you matter most? Who would you miss the most if they were gone? (adapted from Gehart, 2011b, p. 5)

Mapping Hope

As discussed previously in terms of the therapist having hope for their client, hope is a central focus in recovery-oriented work (Davidson et al., 2009). In sharp contrast to previously hopeless perspectives of working with individuals diagnosed with severe mental illness, recovery-oriented work centers in the practitioner believing that the consumer can achieve recovery and engendering hope in the consumer for their recovery. Hopper, Harrison, Janca, and Sartorius (2007) indicate that full or social recovery is a reasonable expectation for the vast majority of individuals diagnosed with severe mental illness. Possible questions for use in mapping hope include the following:

Questions for Mapping Hope

- Do you believe you can lead a "normal" life again? Is this "normal" life something you want?

- As you move forward in your recovery, what parts of your life do you anticipate improving first? What do you expect to be the last to improve? Why?

- How will you know that things are getting better in your life? What will you notice?

- What have you heard or learned about your [diagnosis]? What do you believe? What aspects do you question? (Gehart, 2011b, p. 6)

Mapping Strengths and Resources

As a strengths-based orientation, it makes sense that an important aspect of the assessment includes helping consumers to focus on things that are going well in their life, or times when the problem is not the problem, or when the problem is less severe. However, contrary to what many practitioners expect, mapping strengths can be one of the most difficult aspects of the process (Gehart, 2011b). Fortunately, solution-focused and narrative therapists have laid the groundwork for therapists in the recovery-oriented pursuit to follow. Techniques for mapping strengths and resiliencies include starting therapy by getting to know the person apart from their problem, always looking for exceptions to the problems, and focusing on small signs of change and progress (Bertolino & O'Hanlon, 2002; Cooperrider & Whitney, 2005; De Jong & Berg, 2002; White & Epston, 1990). It becomes the job of the therapist to carefully attend to and listen for the strengths and resources that may not be readily apparent to the consumer or others around them. These strengths are referred to as shadow strengths (Gehart, 2010).

> ### Questions for Mapping Strengths and Resources
>
> - When, where, or with whom are your symptoms not a problem or less severe?
>
> - When do you have the most fun? When are you the least unhappy?
>
> - What unique skills and abilities have you discovered in your current situation and/or on your path to recovery so far?
>
> - What habits or elements of the problem behaviors and thoughts are strengths in another context or in smaller doses? (Gehart, 2011b, p. 6)

Mapping Mental Health

Identifying the mental health diagnosis in the recovery model is an important step in the recovery process. The diagnosis is used to help the practitioner and the consumer to identify possible options for directions in treatment, such as mediation or a specific evidence-based treatment.. Unlike traditional approaches, in recovery-oriented treatment the practitioner and the consumer work together to determine treatment options, jointly considering choices such as medication or no medication, use of psycho-educational interventions or not, or pursuing family involvement in treatment or not. No single approach to recovery is ever forced, rather the consumer selects a path and the therapist respects the consumer's direction while balancing the need for safety. It is the consumer who dictates which options he or she most desires for their journey to recovery.

Recovery Planning: A Collaborative Approach

Recovery planning involves consumer and therapist collaboratively developing goals and strategies for recovery, similar to treatment planning. However, recovery planning differs in that the emphasis is on consumers' identifying their goals and desires while the therapist maintains a helping role, aiding consumers in overcoming barriers to their goals (Davidson et al., 2009). Another important difference in recovery planning as compared to treatment planning is the focus on the person—or the person-centered—nature of the process. Goals and solutions do not always relate to the symptoms or the problems presented in treatment; rather they promote wellness for the client on the client's terms. The recovery plan promotes moving forward in small, concrete steps (Copeland, 2000).

The primary goal in recovery is regaining a meaningful life for the consumer. Goals may include developing new friendships, returning to work, changing living arrangements, and/or reducing medications (Gehart, 2011b). As the practitioner and consumer move through the assessment into the goal setting phase, many of the goals will likely have been revealed throughout the assessment process. Inherent in the process of goal setting is also the necessity for therapists to help manage possible risks associated with goals by working with consumers to develop ways to implement safety plans when necessary. In recovery oriented work, goals are not avoided simply because there is a risk of setback or failure; if the consumer is willing to take the risk, the therapist should work with them to achieve their goal while minimizing possibility of difficulties (Davidson et al., 2009).

The work of the therapist becomes most apparent when they help consumers to break down their goals into small, attainable achievable steps. Therapists may work with consumers to build a "wellness toolbox" that includes lists of useful activities to aid the consumer in moving forward in their recovery along with a daily maintenance plan for implementing the activities (Copeland, 2000; Gehart, 2011b). Consumers map out their days, activity by activity, and develop preventative plans for possible setbacks. In working with consumers, therapists can aid consumers in making minor adjustments or micro-adjustments to daily activities to reduce stress, ensure safety, and promote wellness (Gehart, 2011b). Each small step relates to the long-term goals of the client.

> ## Sample Recovery Plan
>
> Client Goals
>
> 1. Return to work to create sense of purpose and reason for getting up in the morning.
>
>   a. Action step: Volunteer at church
>
>   b. Action step: Participate in supported employment program
>
>   c. Action step: Enroll in community college classes when ready
>
> 2. Reconnect with sister and cousin to regain connection with family.
>
>   a. Action step: Work with therapist to identify past barriers to these relationships and possible solutions.
>
>   b. Action step: Family sessions to facilitate relationship in safe environment.
>
>   c. Action step: Identify a regular means of connecting with family that is comfortable for consumer and family.
>
> 3. Start dating again and develop an intimate friendship/partnership.
>
>   a. Action step: Attend social skills class at Wellness Center.
>
>   b. Action step: Attend dances and social events at Wellness Center and church.
>
>   c. Action step: Use meetings with therapist to discuss social encounters.
>
> 4. Return to horseback riding (favorite hobby).
>
>   a. Action step: Identify local ranch/riding center and offer to volunteer.
>
>   b. Action step: Contact old riding friends to explore possibilities for connection.

Facilitating Recovery: The Interventions

Restorying Identity and Illness Narratives

A key intervention in recovery-oriented practice focuses on re-authoring consumer's identity and illness narratives as well as reducing the impact of problematic dominant discourses about mental illness (Kirkpatrick, 2008; Onken, Craign, Ridgway, Ralph, & Cook, 2007; Roberts, 2000). The concept of re-authoring or rewriting the problem narrative invites consumers to consider a revision

of their problem-saturated story (Gehart, 2010). One way to start the process of deconstructing the effects of being labeled mentally ill is using deconstructive and externalizing questions (Freedman & Combs, 1996; White & Epston, 1990). The reader may notice a theme developing; as with the types of questions used during the assessment period, these questions can help consumers to re-identify with their strengths and life dreams (Gehart, 2011b). Examples of questions to promote restorying include the following:

Questions for Restorying the Identity Narrative

- How has being diagnosed with mental illness changed how you see yourself, your role in relationships, and/or your role in society?

- Do you think being diagnosed with [diagnosis] changes your worth as person? Why or why not? Where do these ideas come from? Do you think they are fair or accurate?

- Do you believe you can still lead a meaningful life with the symptoms you are experiencing? If not, where did you get this idea? If so, how can you make this happen?

Curiosity and Mutual Inquiry

A second and critical intervention for work with consumers in the process of recovery is conversational practices of curiosity and mutual inquiry (Anderson, 1997; Anderson & Gehart, 2007). The not-knowing stance the therapist takes in these healing conversations promotes genuine understanding through the consumer's rich descriptions and personal interpretations of their symptoms. During these conversations, the therapist collaborates with the consumer to explore the consumer's thinking, fears, and hopes in order to open new possibilities for interpreting life events. Additionally, through a process of mutual inquiry, creative and more resources and resourceful ways of responding may be revealed. For example, through mutual inquiry consumers may identify unique interests or talents—such as croquet, cake decorating, or building cuckoo clocks—that may lead to new ideas about to facilitate recovery.

Re-membering Conversations

Oftentimes individuals diagnosed with severe mental illness suffer estrangement from family and friends because of problems related to their symptoms. As noted earlier, building communities of support for consumers is vital in their recovery process. Michael White's re-membering conversations

can be very useful (2007) to help consumers give voice to significant relationships from the past, present, and future. Re-membering conversations invite consumers "to identify who and what has had influence on their identity and to make conscious decisions whether a particular person's influence should be expanded, decreased, or eliminated" (Gehart, 2011b, p. 10). Even if the people are not actually involved in the consumer's life at the current stage, these conversations can help facilitate a sense of connection to significant people. The types of questions utilized in re-membering conversations include:

Re-membering Process

- Identifying a person's contribution to a consumer's life.

- Identifying how the consumer may have affected another's life.

- Articulating how another person may have viewed the consumer's identity.

- Defining the implications for the consumer's identity.

Ethical Implications of Recovery-Oriented Practice

When a therapist works in a recovery-oriented program, they are choosing to step out of the realm of "traditional" therapy. Therapists meet clients where they are, literally, such as their homes, community centers, parks, and cafes. For some therapists, recovery-oriented practice might take place in the car on the way to a doctor's appointment, it may include friends in sessions, or it might involve apartment hunting with a consumer. Occasionally, the relationship stretches the boundaries therapists are accustomed to when therapy has taken place inside the four walls of a private practice or agency setting. It is important for therapists involved in recovery-oriented work to understand from the beginning, that there are not ethical guidelines in place; rather therapists will rely on ethical decision making practices (Gehart, 2011a). In addition to the challenges associated with meeting the consumer where they are, the therapist's boundaries may also be challenged while engaged in the supportive, highly personal journey with another human being—the consumer. The traditional therapeutic role is expanded to include case manager, advocate, mentor, and at times friend. Because the general nature of the relationship with the client is more casual and down to earth, therapists must closely monitor what does harm, what helps, and what does not help a consumer on a case by case basis (Gehart, 2011a). In all likelihood, the ethics involved in recovery-oriented practice will be continually evolving for the practitioner and the field.

Concluding Thoughts

Although recovery-oriented treatment is hailed as a new treatment paradigm (Gehart, 2011a), therapists can nonetheless translate much of their existing knowledge and skills to these new work contexts. Although postmodern therapies are not the only therapeutic approaches with relevance in recovery-oriented treatment, their non-pathologizing philosophies and default strength-based approaches make them one of the most appropriate choices for working within a recovery paradigm. The ideas we outline here should be taken as a starting point and an invitation to embarking on the amazing—often wild and unpredictable—adventures of working with the severe and chronically mentally ill.

References

Adams, N., & Grieder, D. M. (2005). *Treatment planning for person-centered care: The road to mental health and addiction recovery.* New York: Elsevier.

Anderson, H. (1997). *Conversations, language, and possibilities: A postmodern approach to therapy.* New York: Basic Books.

Anderson, H., & Gehart, D. R. (Eds.). (2007). *Collaborative therapy: Relationships and conversations that make a difference.* New York: Brunner-Routledge.

Anderson, H., & Goolishian, H. (1992). *The client is the expert: A not-knowing approach to therapy.* In S. McNamee & K. J. Gergen (Eds.), Therapy as social construction (pp. 25–39). Newbury Park, CA: Sage.

Bertolino, B., & O'Hanlon, B. (2002). *Collaborative, competency-based counseling and therapy.* New York, NY: Allyn & Bacon.

Cooperrider, D. L., & Whitney, D. (2005). *Appreciative inquiry: A positive revolution in change.* San Francisco, CA: Berrett-Koehler Publishers.

Copeland, M. E. (2000). *Wellness recovery action plan.* (Rev. ed.). West Dummerson, VT: Peach Press.

Davidson, L., Tondora, J., O'Connell, M. J., Lawless, M. S., & Rowe, M. (2009). *A practical guide to recovery-oriented practice: Tools for transforming mental health care.* New York: Oxford University Press.

De Jong, P., & Berg, I.K. (2002). *Interviewing for solutions* (2nd ed.). New York, NY: Brooks/Cole.

Eklund, M., Hansson, L, & Ahlqvist, C. (2004). The importance of work as compared to other forms of daily occupations for wellbeing and functionality among persons with long-term mental illness. *Community Mental Health Journal, 40*(5), 465-477.

Freedman, J., & Combs, G. (1996). *Narrative therapy: The social construction of preferred realities.* New York: Norton.

Gehart, D. (2010). *Mastering competencies in family therapy: A practical approach to theory and clinical case documentation.* Pacific Grove, CA: Brooks/Cole.

Gehart, D. (2011a). The mental health recovery movement and family therapy, part I: Consumer-lead reform of services to persons diagnosed with severe mental illness. *Journal of Marital and Family Therapy.* [Early View Version] doi:10.1111/j.1752-0606.2011.00230.x

Gehart, D. (2011b). The mental health recovery movement and family therapy, Part II: A Collaborative, appreciative approach for supporting mental health recovery. *Journal of Marital and Family Therapy.* [Early View Version] doi: 10.1111/j.1752-0606.2011.00229.x

Hopper, K., Harrison, G., Janca, A., & Sartorius, N. (Eds.). (2007). *Recovery from schizophrenia: An international perspective: A report from the WHO Collaborative Project, the international study of schizophrenia.* Oxford: Oxford University Press.

Kirkpatrick, H. (2008). A narrative framework for understanding experiences of people with severe mental illnesses. *Archives of Psychiatric Nursing, 22*(2), 61-68. doi:10.1016/j.apnu.2007.12.002

O'Hanlon, W. H., & Martin, M. (1992). *Solution-oriented hypnosis: An Ericksonian approach.* New York: Norton.

Onken, S. J., Craign, C., Ridgway, P., Ralph, R. O., & Cook, J.A. (2007). An analysis of the definitions and elements of recovery: A review of the literature. P*sychiatric Rehabilitation Journal, 31,* 9-22.

Roberts, G. (2000). Narrative and severe mental illness: What place do stories have in an evidence-based world? *Advances in Psychiatric Treatment, 6,* 432-441.

White, M. (2007). *Maps of narrative practice.* New York: Norton.

White, M., & Epston, D. (1990). *Narrative means to therapeutic ends.* New York: Norton.

PRACTICAL GUIDELINES FOR CASE CONCEPTUALIZATION IN RECOVERY-ORIENTED CARE IN THE PUBLIC SYSTEM

Susan Davis, MS, LMFT

Now that we have an overview of the history and evolution of mental health funding and a comprehensive presentation of the recovery model, we are ready to look at how this shift has affected the way we view and treat clients. The Recovery movement has created a demand for Recovery-oriented services and this has created an impetus for system change (Curtis et al., 1991; Jacobson & Curtis, 2000; New Mexico Human Services, 2004; Roth et al., 1997). Despite these inroads the majority of clinicians continue to provide services based on traditional models. As clinicians we need to adopt treatment that is consistent with the tenets of recovery. Many clinicians were trained using a medical model approach to treatment. Efforts have been made to incorporate the basics of client driven recovery in treatment but these approaches often fall short when clinicians and their supervisors have not successfully integrated an approach containing the elements of recovery. In addition, the treatment demands of community mental health agencies and managed care companies often require language in assessments and treatment plans that focus on symptoms and symptom relief. This focus is often at odds with what is actually occurring in sessions and makes it difficult to incorporate both the intent of recovery and the actual behavioral manifestations that demonstrate the tenets of a Recovery-oriented mental healthcare system.

As Recovery-oriented clinicians our task is to understand the components of recovery and to integrate recovery into treatment. In addition, there is a need to combine Recovery-oriented language in case conceptualization, treatment planning and the documentation needed to comply with our funding sources.

The intent of this Handbook is to assist clinicians in viewing consumers as collaborative members in their treatment and as persons who can live meaningful lives while managing mental health symptoms. To do this we must embrace a complete understanding of the paradigm shift from the medical model to Recovery-oriented care. At this time it is helpful to review the basic tenets of the medical model to better understand how the shift to Recovery-oriented care can and has affected consumers, clinicians and supervisors. Historically, our goal has been to diagnose, develop treatment plans and provide treatment centered on reducing symptoms and returning the client to a previous level of functioning. In the medical model mental illness is viewed as a chronic illness that would require occasional acute services. We didn't expect clients to get well and we communicated that message to them. Treatment was centered on attempting to keep that person stable enough to avoid

hospitalization. The client was to follow the treatment we designed for them and as a result they became dependent on us for problem solving and management of their illness. It is no wonder clients continued to feel helpless and hopeless. Clients were cautioned against putting themselves in situations that might add stress to their lives, lest it precipitate an acute episode. After experiencing Recovery-oriented care one person put it this way:

"I let the symptoms of my illness become the centre of my universe, and symptoms of my illness aren't the centre of my universe anymore" (Amering & Schmolke, 2009, p. 21).

It is no wonder that clients sometimes seemed to look to us to "wave a magic wand" and exact a cure, while they passively and obediently attempted to adhere to our treatment dictates. As "transformed" clinicians we hope to internalize the components of recovery so that we can utilize methods and beliefs that will successfully engage clients in the exciting and empowering process of recovery and the collaborative management of their own mental health.

To add to the complexity, there is often a rather urgent "message" from funding sources who do view treatment from the medical model, to make sure symptoms of the diagnosis have been reduced or eliminated and the GAF (Global Assessment of Functioning) has been improved by our interventions. If the initial GAF for a client was 45, which would indicate that the client had serious impairment in social, occupational, or school functioning and had suicidal ideation or obsessive behaviors, then improvement would be indicated by an increase in the GAF. A GAF of 60 would indicate moderate symptoms and moderate impairment in functioning thereby indicating an improvement in symptoms. For many years, the success of treatment has been determined by this standard and it continues today.

First, we will review the basics of case conceptualization and how we add an overlay of Recovery-oriented mental health care to our existing theoretical orientations. We will review the basic components of case conceptualization and how that differs from clinical assessment. Secondly, we will move to understanding how treatment plans can be transformed to include the client's view of what is needed to meet their goals for treatment. Finally, we will look at the complexity of documentation that is needed to meet the requirements for reimbursement from multiple funding sources and how that relates to the language of recovery.

Case Conceptualization

For seasoned clinicians case conceptualization occurs almost unconsciously. Having integrated a framework for understanding the client's presenting problems, how the problems affect the client's

ability to function, the severity of the impairment and how they affect or are affected by the client's environment, their relationships with others, and finally assessing risk to the client and others, the clinician will develop a hypothesis of what is happening with the client. This may happen seemingly without conscious thought, while at the same time this information will be embedded into the theoretical framework or frameworks in which they prefer to work.

For our purposes here we will review the basic components of case conceptualization. We will also make a distinction between case conceptualization and clinical assessment. Although they often contain the same or similar information, clinical assessment has its purpose in determining diagnosis, and assessment of the severity of symptoms and risk factors. Case conceptualization on the other hand is theoretical. It allows us to view our client's impairments through the eyes of family systems therapy (Gehart, 2010). Or in the case of other disciplines, the clinician will view the client's impairments through the eyes of their preferred orientation.

Case Conceptualization and assessment are very similar initially. We begin by collecting information about the following:

- Client's demographics
- Referral source
- Circumstances causing Client to seek help if self-referred
- Presenting problem
- Current level of functioning
- Risk assessment self/others
- School and work history
- Medical history
- Legal history
- Substance history
- Mental health/psychiatric history
- Family and social relationships (current)
- Family and social relationships (history)

For a clinical assessment we use this information to form a diagnosis. Most funding sources require that we provide a five-axis diagnosis as found in the Diagnostic and Statistical manual (see below). By using the information gathered from the list above, we will have the information needed to provide a complete five-axis diagnosis for the client.

Axis I Clinical Disorder

Axis II Personality Disorder or Mental Retardation

Axis III General Medical Conditions

Axis IV Psychosocial Or Environmental Problems

Axis V Global Assessment of Functioning

We use this information to develop a Case Conceptualization and create a hypothesis of the origin of the problem, how and why we think it developed as it did, what areas of the client's life are most affected and what we and the client think needs to change to relieve these symptoms (Goals). This is an important point in case conceptualization because it is also the beginning of the development of treatment goals. We are beginning to provide a link between the Presenting Problems and the Treatment Plan (sometimes referred to as the Recovery Plan). And finally, we take all this information and examine it from different theoretical perspectives. Looking at the problem from different theoretical perspectives adds an additional dimension to our case conceptualization. When we integrate our theoretical perspective with the client's treatment plan and case conceptualization, we gradually form a roadmap for the client's journey toward recovery.

By adding the overlay of Recovery-oriented treatment to case conceptualization, we begin to configure the information we have gathered in a different way. From the beginning we are looking at how we can communicate to the client that they have the ability to decide the direction of their own recovery and that they know the best way to get there. The clinician will support the client in identifying goals and strengths. At first, this may be difficult for both the clinician and the client. They may both see only the symptoms of the diagnosis and the negative impact on the client. Initially, it may be difficult for the clinician to trust that the client knows what they need. When a clinician feels this way it is often because they have an underdeveloped case conceptualization, which has not led them to treatment goals. The client who is more familiar with treatment from the medical model may feel the clinician is not doing their "job" or be anxious that they themselves do not know how to identify what they need.

This is the time for the clinician to talk to the client about Recovery-oriented care. A better understanding of the approach will assist the client in viewing treatment from a different perspective. We must not assume that since we have changed the way we provide treatment from a medical model to Recovery-oriented care, that this will not impact clients, who have for years received treatment

in another way. Just as it takes time and repetition for us to make the shift, so will the client need to "see" how Recovery-oriented care is different from previous approaches. The clinician must support the client's goals while using their own professional skills to identify impairments that may stand in the way of the client's goals and to assist them in forging a path through the impairments to the desired goal. It is the responsibility of the clinician to be helpful, supportive and hopeful.

Typically we begin by asking clients to describe how they have been affected by the problem or events. We query them about their symptoms and coping strategies and hopefully seek out client strengths. Unfortunately, although we have been asked to add strengths to our assessments in the past, they have played a relatively small part in treatment. Recovery-oriented care assists the clients in viewing themselves differently. For example, where they may have previously viewed themselves as a depressed person who could not function in the world without overtaxing themselves emotionally, we are asking them to see themselves as a person who can function while managing depression or other symptoms. We can see how clients' perceptions of themselves and how we think of them affect our interactions with them and what we believe is possible for them.

These perceptions change when we integrate strengths early in our case conceptualization and treatment planning. Looking at strengths through the lens of Recovery-oriented treatment allows us to be more creative. The following table demonstrates how symptoms can be reframed to help identify strengths and to collaborate with the client in how best to use those strengths. Looking at the "flip-side" of symptoms also helps clients begin to view themselves in a more positive light.

	Possible Associated Strength
Depression	• Awareness of what others think and feel • Connected to others and/or desires connection • Has dreams and hopes • Has had the courage to take action to realize dreams • Realistic assessment of self/others (according to recent research; Seligman, 2004)
Anxiety	• Pays attention to details • Desires to perform well • Careful and thoughtful about actions • Able to plan for future and anticipate potential obstacles

	Possible Associated Strength
Arguing	• Stands up for self and/or beliefs • Fights injustice • Wants the relationship to work • Has hope for better things for others/self
Anger	• In touch with feelings and thoughts • Stands up against injustice • Believes in fairness • Able to sense their boundaries and when they are crossed
Overwelmed	• Concerned about others' needs • Thoughtful • Able to see the big picture • Sets goals and pursues them

By permission of Gehart, D. (2010). *Mastering competencies in family therapy: A practical approach to theory and clinical case documentation.* Pacific Grove, CA: Wadsworth/Brook Cole.

We can use the strengths associated with different emotional states to move the therapeutic process forward by encouraging the client to see how those strengths can help develop coping and problem-solving skills and how to view problems and symptoms in a strength-based manner. By observing the attributes associated with their feelings, clients are able to shift to a different perspective and become expert in developing personal ways of responding to problems.

The Recovery-oriented conceptual components are described below. By understanding each one we are able to integrate them into case conceptualization and utilize them in our work with our clients in a positive and collaborative way, which supports their growth.

Hope is essential for recovery: As clinicians we can be alert to the parallel process that develops between the client and ourselves and in turn between supervisors and clinicians. A clinician may mirror the client's sense of hopelessness. Hope is not just optimism but a belief in the client's willingness to persevere through uncertainty and setbacks. This belief in recovery is communicated to the client to help develop a belief in his or her own recovery process.

Recovery is non-linear: Recovery is a process that is based on continual growth, occasional setbacks, and learning from experience. This process may involve grieving lost time, opportunities

or relationships. It may mean that social skills and work skills need to be learned or relearned. Both the client and the clinician understand that there may be ups and downs in the client's recovery. When recovery is understood as non-linear, there is a greater understanding of the need to expand a client's awareness of personal strengths as well as their needs. As clinicians who understand this process, we can assist clients in rebuilding their lives in a more satisfying manner and in developing skills to deal with setbacks. Recovery means that the person is no longer defined by the diagnosis; rather, he or she is a person with an illness that periodically requires attention.

Recovery means responsibility: Clinicians are encouraged to allow and ask each client to take personal responsibility for his or her own treatment. The clinician needs to communicate to the client that they will take on increasing responsibility for their own care in order to reach the goals they have developed. As we move away from the medical model, this paradigm shift becomes more important. This is an area that has been difficult for both the client and the therapist. Struggling to move away from the medical model requires the therapist to have faith in the client's abilities. The clinician is at risk of falling back and feeling the need to take responsibility for the client, especially if the client is struggling. Clients are at risk at this point of losing confidence in their own abilities and perhaps wanting to return to a time when they had less responsibility for their own mental health.

Recovery requires respect: When we take responsibility for the client's treatment, we are disrespecting the client's own abilities. The Recovery-oriented clinician respects the client's right to have control of his/her own mental health treatment. This does not mean that we recommend saying to the client "It is not my job to be responsible for your mental health;" rather, we communicate a desire to assist the client in maintaining their goals and relying on the problem solving skills they have developed.

Recovery is holistic: Recovery addresses a person's whole life, including mind, body, and spirit. The clinician's work with the client involves assistance in seeking support, maintaining health, developing work habits and skills, identifying resources, and developing relationships that are supportive. The clinician may feel challenged by the increased involvement in client care, which necessitates more case management and at times challenges our previous understanding of boundaries. The development of supports outside of "therapy" contributes to positive outcomes. Clients have reported that involvement in peer-to-peer relationships, seeking out peer relationships in community settings such as clubhouses or wellness centers, having a pet and exploring faith in God, have all contributed to their recovery. Treatment providers need to remind clients of the resources outside of traditional treatment that can significantly add to recovery. In Recovery-oriented treatment clients are not one-dimensional; they are more than their symptoms. It is our job to view them that way and help clients to see themselves as multi-dimensional.

Public System Practical Guidelines for Treatment Planning and Documentation

This section presents documentation and treatment planning together, as they are part of the thread that we weave through a client's chart beginning with the assessment, moving to treatment planning and finally to progress notes and termination summaries. Although this section will address conceptual changes necessary for creating Recovery-oriented treatment plans, this cannot be addressed without acknowledging that we must meet the documentation requirements of our payers and oversight organizations that often determine whether services will be reimbursed. These organizations include but are not limited to insurance companies, managed care companies, preferred provider organizations and state and county mental health providers. Many funding sources will determine whether a service is covered based on "medical necessity."

Medical necessity is a term that describes medical or clinical activities that are justified as reasonable, necessary and/or appropriate, based on evidence-based clinical standards of care. Another way of saying this is that in order to meet "medical necessity" you must have a diagnosis and there are services or treatments for this diagnosis that meet acceptable standards of medical practice. An example would be appendicitis. If your appendix is inflamed, it is a usual practice to remove it surgically. Many people have had their appendix removed, so surgery to remove it is considered to "meet acceptable standards of medical practice," and therefore meets the criteria for medical necessity. This criterion is different for different payers. Managed care companies usually have a committee that approves a diagnosis and will have a standard list that designates the number of visits needed to eliminate that problem. In mental health treatment, for instance, the standard for first time major depression without psychotic features might be defined as: a) A covered diagnosis and b) Expected treatment episode to resolve in 8 individual sessions with a psychotherapist and 3 medical appointments with a psychiatrist.

Community mental health agencies and other government-supported clinics require that their definition of medical necessity is followed for services to be covered; in many cases these government oversight entities can demand refunds of funds for services they determine were not covered or where documentation did not meet the standards for medical necessity. It is then understandable why documentation takes on such a great import and why it is important to document using language that communicates clearly what was wrong, what we did, why we did it and the outcome of the treatment. Again, we weave a thread from assessment, case conceptualization, treatment planning, progress notes (session notes) and finally to the termination summary.

It is no wonder that documentation of assessments, treatment plans and progress notes becomes a focus of much concern at all levels of Behavioral Health. Sometimes the requirements for

documentation are at odds with Recovery-oriented thinking and documentation. This presents a dilemma for clinicians and their supervisors. Treatment plans that meet medical necessity and oversight audit requirements are often written to demonstrate the intent to reduce or eliminate behaviors related to the diagnosis. For example, a depressed person presents as only sleeping 3 hours a night. A treatment goal for this client might be to increase sleeping from 3 hours to 7 hours a night. Sleeping 7 hours a night would represent significant improvement in that symptom of major depression. Some treatment plan forms are even designed to meet these requirements, using a fill-in-the-blanks form and do not allow space for the language of recovery. This is a conundrum that such agencies, which are making the shift to Recovery-oriented treatment, will have to address with their oversight organizations. Until then, clinicians and supervisors can create a more client-driven treatment plan as part of their progress notes.

Medical Necessity Requirements:

In order to meet the requirements of medical necessity, treatment must have the following components:

- Culturally Competent. Culturally competent services include a set of congruent behaviors, attitudes and policies to enable effective service provision in cross cultural settings. These behaviors, attitudes and policies are designed to foster a climate that will provide services that recognize and are sensitive to cultural diversity.

- Covered Diagnosis (Title 9, Section 1830.205). Most Axis I diagnoses are accepted. Examples of non-covered diagnoses include Mental Retardation, Autistic disorders, and Dementia.

- Impairments resulting from the principal diagnosis.

- Interventions must address the impairments resulting from the covered diagnosis.

- One of the following impairments must be present as a result of the diagnosis: for adults, a significant impairment in an important area of life functioning and a reasonable probability of significant deterioration in an important area of life functioning; for children, a reasonable probability they will not progress as developmentally appropriate.

- Interventions are also defined and there should be a reasonable expectation that the intervention will diminish impairment or prevent significant impairment in an important area of life functioning.

Clearly we can see how difficult it is for the clinician to integrate the language of recovery into treatment plans and documentation. Treatment plans are often viewed as a necessary evil that must be completed so the clinician can get down to the business of providing therapy to a person who may have little resemblance to what has been written about them. Clinicians and supervisors must make a concentrated effort with the client's help to translate what the client is requesting and needing into a treatment plan that meets medical necessity. It is understandable that clinicians and supervisors are conflicted as to how to document medical necessity and at the same time write Recovery-oriented treatment plans. The following information proposes what constitutes a good client-driven recovery plan.

Architecture is an example of a profession in which planning activities are essential to the practice and a successful outcome, and an area in which the central role of the client is understood. Despite the fact that the client lacks the professional and technical ability to design and construct a building, the architect understands that it is his or her role to make sure that the client's needs, wishes, and dreams are included in the planning process. When we use the example of the architect who listens to what the family wants in style, size, configuration and lifestyle and we apply the same concept to what our clients want out of treatment, we will be heading in the right direction to create a good treatment plan. It is a given that the client's expectations will be clearly visible in the final outcome (Adams & Grieder, 2005, p. 4).

When clients enter therapy they typically come in telling us what is wrong. They aren't sleeping, they cry frequently and feel like they don't enjoy anything and to top it off, they are not getting along with their boss, husband, sister, mother, etc. They usually do not say to us: "I am experiencing an episode of recurrent major depression, I need you to give me hope that my life will get better and to understand that under this depression I am a person with hopes and dreams" and "I think I need to access my strengths and to grieve what this illness has taken away from me over the years." Transformed clinicians use the information provided by the client and incorporate this information into a conceptualization that will help determine if the service is one that the client's payer considers medically necessary. This is then incorporated into a format that fits with our theoretical orientation, and finally, viewed through the lens of Recovery-oriented treatment.

Clinicians frequently feel overwhelmed by this complicated but necessary process. Recovery-oriented treatment and the need for Recovery-oriented treatment plans are often presented to clinicians by managers or clinic supervisors who have embraced the concept of recovery but are not able to help translate it for the clinician into language that will assist them in changing how they provide treatment and document goals. Clinicians scratch their heads, if we ask the client what their goals are we might hear them say, "I want to feel better" or "I want to buy a house of my own" or "I

want to finish my education." How can that show up on a treatment plan? The difficulty with this concept initially is that it seems to imply that the therapist's professional abilities take a backseat to the client's wishes. Initially there was much confusion among clinicians as they tried to put aside their "medical model brains" and provide treatment based on the client's wishes; however, this is a misconception of the approach.

A clinician new to Recovery-oriented care describes her process in translating a client's goal into a format that fits well with Recovery-oriented care and meets medical necessity this way:

"A client came into treatment and stated her goal of treatment was to "buy a house." I remember thinking I did not have a clue how to incorporate the client's goal to buy a house with the diagnosis of major depression and my knowledge that this client was receiving state aid to survive. I knew that this goal would not be acceptable to our payers! However, after thinking for a moment I asked myself, 'What would this client need to be different in order for her to work toward her goal of buying a house?' I could immediately see that the client would need to be less depressed, she would need to go to school or get a skill so she could get a job and she would need a job so she could start to save toward buying a house. She would also need support to do this and someone who believed that she could do it."

This clinician was responding to the client as a person and not as an illness. She didn't say "Oh, she really can't do this, you know, she is chronically depressed." Instead she began to see the client as a person with needs and wants and wishes for a better life, someone whom this clinician could help by assisting her in redefining who she was and to whom she could provide hope and support. Without realizing it the clinician was empowering the client, looking at her strengths instead of just her problems, providing her with hope and respect, and supporting the client in taking responsibility for changing her life. By suggesting that she would need to go to school and get a job she was taking a step toward viewing recovery as holistic. The clinician used her professional knowledge to identify: 1) The client's diagnosis (which she needed in order to meet medical necessity); 2) The level of impairment from the mental health diagnosis; 3) The mental health barriers that stood between the client and her stated goal; 4) The assistance or case management that might be needed to help the client move toward her goal; 5) The Recovery-oriented care that would support her goals.

Understanding Recovery-oriented care from this perspective makes it relatively simple to determine how we would document care. Treatment goals will meet medical necessity and will find their way to the recovery or treatment plans, in the usual manner, to make the goals acceptable for payment from payers. The documentation of Recovery-oriented care will be noted in the body of progress notes and termination summaries, along with increase or decrease of symptoms. This is

where we will document the collaborative work between the clinician and the client. Documentation that accurately describes a treatment intervention, why you intervened in this way and how the intervention is related to one of the treatment goals will ensure payment by most payers.

For example, you have accompanied "Jacob" to the clubhouse. One of his treatment goals is to increase socialization/reduce isolation. He has difficulty entering new social situations and sometimes has panic attacks. You have been teaching him relaxation techniques to use in public situations. In your progress notes you will state that you accompanied him to the Clubhouse to reduce his anxiety about entering new places alone and to assist him in using his relaxation techniques in public to avoid a panic attack. You are describing recovery-oriented care and tying it to the treatment goals. When you make this link you are able to bill for this service. If you said you went with the client to the clubhouse because he was afraid to go alone and you wanted him to increase his socialization, you would most likely not meet the criteria for that service to be paid.

Approaching documentation in this way allows us to support clients as they envision their lives along Recovery-oriented lines. We build on our client's goals and wishes. The work can begin with helping them realize that their goals are even possible and that they can look outside of their illness to a different reality. This work is not different from what we do when we conceptualize a case and fit the symptoms of the client into a theory or group of theories in order to reduce symptoms by working at their core. In the case of recovery we bond the tenets of recovery to our theoretical orientations.

Thinking in terms of Recovery-oriented care allows us to document recovery concepts in the same way that we would document our theoretical conceptualization of the treatment. An example of a family systems documentation may be that we met with the child's parents to "reduce the polarization of discipline" between them in order to help provide cohesive discipline that will be more effective. For Recovery-oriented care we document how we encouraged hope, empowered the client, facilitated peer-to-peer relationships and assisted the client in taking responsibility for their own care. Thinking of recovery in the same manner that we document our interventions in the progress notes removes the burden of how we will ensure that the interventions are recorded and in doing so we continue to integrate recovery into treatment and into our thinking. Thus, the job of the clinician is to become familiar with and to integrate the concept of recovery in a clear way so that they are able to use recovery along with their theoretical case conceptualization and documentation of medical necessity.

Defining what is needed in order to begin treatment is not as easy as it sounds. It is our job as clinicians to develop goals based on the client's wishes. In Treatment Planning for Person-Centered Care, The Road to Mental Health and Addiction Recovery (2005), Neal Adams and Diane Grieder

divide client goals into three levels: Life goals, Service or treatment goals, and Quality of life enhancement goals.

Life goals often include an individual's aspirations and hopes for overall improvement in their lives. A client may say he wants to finish his education, buy a house, get married or have a relationship. Service or treatment goals are linked to the mental health concerns that brought that client into treatment. These goals are often used to determine discharge criteria. A treatment goal for a client who is experiencing difficulty sleeping due to depression, may be for that client to sleep 6 to 7 hours per night for a period of one month. Reaching that goal would indicate the client's depression has decreased. Quality of life enhancement goals are often more subjective, and may not seem to be directly related to the treatment goals. An example would be a parent who says "I just want our family to be happier." Often the implication is that a behavior or mental health issue attributed to the identified patient is preventing the family from being happier.

Using designations of this type can be helpful in recognizing the different goal distinctions that exist in a client's choice of treatment goals. Clearly the service goals are comparable to our "Medical Model" goals and are most likely to be the goals required by our payers. Life goals and Enhancement goals may be where many clients begin in treatment. "I want to feel happier," "I want to get along better with my husband," "and "I want my child to be successful in school."

When we consider these goals, the key difference between them is that enhancement goals may not be related to treatment whereas life goals may be. A goal of a Recovery-oriented clinician is to think beyond the medical model reduction of symptoms, to incorporate Recovery-oriented principles into treatment and into supervision, and to view clients as people with hopes and dreams that may have been buried under the message that he or she is mentally ill and therefore incapable of achieving life dreams.

In Summary

As we expand our ability to conceptualize a holistic view of client care, it becomes easier to see how the tenets of recovery are not just concepts but rather a shift toward a more hopeful, collaborative approach to mental health care. When we embrace this paradigm, we can see the concept in its totality and the separate parts of Recovery-oriented care become an integrated approach in which we collaborate with our clients. In this collaboration we apply our professional experience to map out the road with our clients to meet their goals. Just as the architect uses skills to interpret the client's stated needs, so does the clinician use skills to encourage clients to participate and manage their health care needs in order to meet their goals. We cannot achieve success in recovery if we do not understand that this model encompasses a more compassionate, hopeful presentation to the

client and at the same time draws them into a collaborative effort with the clinician in which they are given permission and expected to participate.

Recovery-oriented care is an overlay upon our already existing models. Just as we search through the client's words looking for various theoretical components and interventions, we will now be adding to that the components of Recovery-oriented care. We inject statements that give the client hope that they have the strengths to do what they need to do to heal or get better. Our supportive care empowers the client to move forward. We help them to understand that their illness will have ups and downs and will be non-linear. We encourage them to take personal responsibility for their health and respect that they know what they need. We encourage them to find, develop, or return to an environment that provides a sense of belonging, whether it is the local mental health Clubhouse, or a social, religious or work group, so that they can have the support of peers. And finally we look at the client in his or her totality and view their treatment as holistic.

Since many of these qualities of care already exist in our current models of treatment, they may seem artificial or contrived when we try to use them. Clinicians and supervisors get confused when skills are relabeled and think that it is a difficult task to incorporate these attitudes and changes and to allow the client to take control of their care. What is very important about Recovery-oriented care is that we now need to consciously consider these attributes and attitudes toward respectful treatment and we are given permission to help our clients grow. We no longer need to be constrained by a medical model view of treatment. As clinicians we can allow ourselves to soar and give our clients the type of care that we are trained to give. We are given permission and even a mandate to perceive the client as part of a system and to support their functioning in that system. When we reframe Recovery-oriented care, we see it for what it really is and as clinicians we can welcome it for ourselves and our clients.

Discussion Questions: Case Conceptualization

1. Describe and compare the Medical Model of treatment to Recovery-oriented care.

2. What are the pros and cons of each of the above models?

3. How does Recovery-oriented care benefit the client?

4. If you are using a family systems theory to work with your client, can you still use recovery principles? Give an example.

5. What is the difference between case conceptualization and assessment? How are they similar?

Discussion Questions: Treatment Planning and Documentation

1. How can identifying the client's strengths early in treatment impact how you feel about the client? Would knowing the client's strengths impact treatment?

2. What does medical necessity mean? How can medical necessity impact reimbursement for services provided?

3. How do Life goals differ from Service or Treatment goals?

4. Can you describe how you would "build a bridge" from a Life goal to a Service or Treatment goal?

References

Adams, N., & Grieder, D. M., (2005). *Treatment Planning for Person-Centered Care, The Road to Mental Health and Addiction Recovery*. London, UK: Elsevier Academic Press.

American Psychiatric Association, (2000). *Diagnostic and Statistical Manual, IV-TR*. Published by the American Psychiatric Association.

Davidson, L., Tondora, J., Lawless, M. S., O'Connell, M. J., & Rowe, M. (2006). *A Practical Guide to Recovery oriented Practice*. New York: Oxford University Press.

Davidson, L., Harding, C., & Spaniol, L. (Ed.) (2005). *Recovery From Severe Mental Illnesses Research Evidence and Implications for Practice*. Boston University, Boston: Center for Psychiatric Rehabilitation.

Gehart, D. (2010). *Mastering competencies in family therapy: A practical approach to theory and clinical case documentation*. Pacific Grove, CA: Wadsworth/Brook Cole.

Linhorst, D. M. (2006). *Empowering People with Severe Mental Illness, A Practical Guide*. New York: Oxford University Press, Inc.

Moline, M. E. (1998). *Documenting psychotherapy: Essentials for mental health practitioners*. Thousand Oaks, California: Sage Publications, Inc.

BOUNDARIES AND ETHICAL CONSIDERATIONS: AM I DOING THE RIGHT THING? ETHICAL DECISION MAKING IN A RECOVERY MODEL

Stephen W. Brown, Ph.D., J.D.

Mental health recovery models emphasize client autonomy, shared decision making, client and family empowerment, independent community functioning and provider advocacy. These recovery principles are socially and clinically desirable; however, they are different from the traditional "provider-client hierarchical" relationship that has been practiced for many years. We now face situations where some of our coworkers and students are recovering from a mental illness; where a client's treatment choices are not the choice we would recommend; and we are expected to advocate for the mentally ill while we have no education or training in advocacy. These situations, and others, provide ethical dilemmas that we have not had to address in the past.

The AAMFT Code of Ethics (AAMFT, 2001), the CAMFT Code of Ethics (CAMFT, 2011) and Consultation are still the tried and true ethical problem solving tools. However, the ethical dilemmas that we now face seem to require a deeper probing into our own ethical values. Thus, the purpose of this section is to encourage you to explore and clarify your own professional ethical value system as it relates to working in a recovery model. We will start by examining two different models of ethical problem solving; one method focuses on the consequences of our behavior and the other focuses on the morality of our behavior. Then, I will share five professional ethical principles that I use when practicing recovery. Lastly, we ask you to identify the key values that underlie your own professional ethics as you practice in a recovery model.

Results-Oriented Ethics and Behavior-Oriented Ethics in Recovery

Results-Oriented Ethics (Consequential Ethics)

Consequential ethics states that ethical behaviors must have positive consequences. Consequential ethics does not consider the morality of the acts we perform; rather it only considers the results or consequence of our behavior. Thus, consequential ethics is often summarized as "the ends justify the means." In a recovery approach, we need to consider the positive consequences and the best interests of multiple stakeholders including clients, family members, support systems, the community and practitioners. Utilitarianism is a type of consequential ethics that evaluates positive consequences using a multi-systemic approach. That is, a good act is defined as one that brings the most benefit to the most people. As applied to a recovery model, utilitarianism requires ethical decision to consider

the best interests of multiple stakeholders including the client, the family, the support system, the community and the practitioner. It would be fantastic if all of our behaviors were in everyone's best interest; however, this is seldom the case. Thus, from a utilitarian perspective we need to somehow choose behaviors that we believe will bring the most good to the most people and the least harm to the fewest people.

> *Consequential Ethics Example:* When asked by a client if she ever deliberately hurt herself, a therapist might change the subject or lie to avoid self-disclosure about this topic. The therapist believed that admitting a history of self-abuse might convey a message that self-abuse was acceptable behavior. This therapist believed that the tactic of not being completely open and honest about this topic would produce the most benefit for the client, the family, the support system, the community and herself.

Moral Behavior Ethics (Deontological Ethics)

Moral behavior or deontological ethics is the ethical theory that there are behaviors that are clearly ethical and there are other behaviors that are clearly unethical. As an example, in deontological ethics, telling the truth is moral, telling a lie is wrong. In deontological ethics the consequences of an act are unimportant; thus deontological ethics may be summarized as "do the right thing, no matter what the consequences." As ethical MFTs we have a duty to engage in moral behavior. Helping a client would be a correct or moral behavior; harming a client would be an incorrect or amoral behavior. In the recovery model at times it may be difficult to identify the moral behavior. As an example in some cultures expressing strong emotions is acceptable and expected behavior, thus an MFT would encourage a client from this culture to express his emotions strongly. However, in other cultures stoicism is acceptable and desirable behavior, encouraging a client from this culture to express his feelings strongly would be contraindicated. Clearly, encouraging strong emotional expression would not be a universally correct behavior; however, understanding, respecting and practicing consistently with a client's culture would always be moral behavior.

> *Deontological Ethics Example:* When asked by a client if she ever deliberately hurt herself, a therapist honestly answered that at one point in her life she had engaged in this behavior. This therapist believed that being open and honest was the moral thing to do. (This therapist also believed that the self-disclosure would facilitate the therapeutic relationship and would instill hope in the client that she too could recover.)

My Recovery-Oriented Professional Ethics

There are many personal and professional values that underlie MFT recovery practice. These values guide our lives, they determine what we do, how we do it and they strongly influence our perception of ourselves and others. In this section I present my personal ethical values as they apply to the recovery model. Since these are my values and beliefs, I am writing this section in a first person narrative.

As a teacher and practitioner of recovery I have many values that permeate my behavior. These values are not different from my everyday living values; however, in a recovery model I am especially sensitive to their implications. The six primary values that seem most relevant to my recovery philosophy are: do no harm, benevolence, respect, integrity, responsibility and being a mensch. These are discussed briefly below.

Do no harm – This ethical principle requires that I never intentionally cause harm to my students, my clients, my coworkers or my employer. It is better to do nothing than to do the wrong thing. It is better to do less safely than to do more and encounter a risk.

Benevolence – This principle tells me to do things with compassion and empathy. As a professional, who follows the Golden Rule, I attempt to treat the people with whom I work as I would like to be treated.

Respect – The principle says that I attempt to behave in ways that demonstrate respect for the dignity and worth of all people. I strive to do things that help people enhance their sense of self-worth and self-respect. I maintain confidences. I seek to understand cultural differences and I strive to behave in ways that show respect for people, their culture and their uniqueness.

Integrity – Following this principle I attempt to deal honestly and fairly in all of my professional activities. I attempt to always keep my promises, I do not intentionally misrepresent facts and I do not engage in deceitful behaviors. While in some instances it might be necessary for me to engage in deception, I only do so when the benefits of such actions clearly and substantially outweigh the risk of harm.

Responsibility – I recognize and accept the responsibilities that are inherent in my education, training and professional positions. I do not engage in improper dual relationships and I strive to avoid conflicts of interest. I strive to act in ways that bring honor to my profession and I accept responsibility for the results of my actions.

Being a Mensch – Mensch is a Yiddish term that refers to acting in ways that bring pride to the people who care about me. I strive to do the right thing in all situations; I strive to always practice the values described above; I strive not to overvalue my own importance; I strive to learn from my mistakes and I attempt to forgive myself for the mistakes I make.

Clarifying Your Own Recovery Values

Thinking about recovery, the clients with whom you will work, the goals of your program and the issues you will face, what are the fundamental values you intend to follow when practicing in a recovery model? Some of your values may be the same as mine, others may be different. Please take a few minutes to think about recovery as you understand it and then think about the ethics you want to use in your practice. Use the space below to write the basic values you intend to hold as you practice following a recovery model.

PRACTICE WITH ETHICAL DECISION-MAKING

Adapted by Kathy Wexler from "A New Model of Ethical Reasoning for Recovery-Oriented Care" presented at the 2010 AAMFT Annual Conference by Benjamin E. Caldwell, Linna Wang, Marsha L. Michaels, and Stephen W. Brown.

In the following scenarios, assume that you are clinician working in a community mental health agency that has adopted principles of recovery-oriented care. What decision would you make? Why?

Some Recommended Steps in Decision-Making:

The overall question is, "Does this action/choice support the consumer's recovery?"

1. What is the expressed preference of the consumer? (e.g., "I want a hug.")

2. What history, background or relevant information do you have about the consumer that might influence your decision? (e.g., the consumer has a history of sexual abuse, and might sexualize the hug. Or, the consumer's psychotic symptoms might cause them to misunderstand the hug.)

3. What are the rules, guidelines or role expectations in your setting? (e.g., some agencies have a rule about not touching at all, in order to avoid complications.)

4. What are your own preferences or choices? (e.g., hugging would make you uncomfortable.)

5. Consultation—with colleagues or supervisors—always a good idea. Not always possible in the moment when decisions must be made.

6. Consider the consequences of NOT acting. (e.g., consumer feels rejected, missed opportunity to experience non-exploitive touch, etc.)

7. Take an action (Hug or don't hug)

8. Evaluate the results

9. Make corrections if appropriate

VIGNETTE A: It is raining, and you are leaving the agency for the night. A consumer, not your client but someone that you know, calls to you in the parking lot. She asks you for a ride to the bus stop. Will you give her a lift?

VIGNETTE B: A consumer who has struggled with drug addiction says he has a very bad headache. He knows you have some aspirin or Tylenol in your desk. He asks you for a couple of pills so he can get through the group meeting.

VIGNETTE C: There is a basketball hoop at the recreation center used by your agency. You are a very gifted player, and you are shooting hoops with some consumers who are also very good. Someone suggests putting a few dollars in the pot and playing for money. Do you participate?

VIGNETTE D: A consumer in one of your groups designs and makes jewelry from recyclables. She brings samples to show to the group. She asks for support and advice in selling the jewelry. One particular necklace really appeals to you. Do you offer to buy it?

For more information:

American Association for Marriage and Family Therapy. (2005). *Code of ethics.* Washington, DC: Author.

American Counseling Association. (2005). *ACA code of ethics.* Retrieved from http://www.counseling. org/Resources/CodeOfEthics/TP/Home/CT2.aspx

American Psychological Association. (2002). Ethical principles of psychologists and code of conduct. *American Psychologist, 57*(12), 1060– 1073. doi:10.1037/0003-066X.57.12.1060

California Association of Marriage and Family Therapists. (2009). *[Code of ethics part 1].* Retrieved from http://www.camft.org/Content/NavigationMenu/AboutCAMFT/CodeofEthicsPartI/ CodeOfEthicsPartI.pdf

Hendricks, B., Bradley, L. J., Southern, S., Oliver, M. &; Birdsall, B. (2011). Ethical code for the International Association of Marriage and Family Counselors. *Family Journal, 19*(2), 217-224, doi:10.1177/1066480711400814

Homer, R. & Kelly, T. B. (2007). Ethical decision-making in the helping profession: A contextual and caring approach. *Journal of Religion & Spirituality in Social Work, 26*(1), 71-88. doi:10.1300/ J377v26n0105

APPLYING LAWS AND ETHICS IN RECOVERY-ORIENTED TREATMENT SETTINGS: TEXTS OF RELEVANT CODES FOR REFERENCE AND DISCUSSION

Assembled by Kathy Wexler, M.A, LMFT

Students and interns know how important it is to understand the laws and ethical standards governing mental health professions, and have every intention of practicing within accepted guidelines. However, existing standards have built-in assumptions that may appear to be inconsistent with recovery principles. Reviewing the language of documents such as the weekly log of experience, or the supervisors' responsibility statement suggests that certain ideas seem deeply embedded. If they were to be verbalized, these ideas might be:

1. There is a specific procedure called "psychotherapy." Psychotherapy is a procedure delivered by experts to patients/clients who need "treatment."

2. For the welfare of the people being treated, the experts must keep a professional distance. There are clear rules about how much personal disclosure is appropriate, and how roles can overlap.

3. "Psychotherapy" happens in officially designated places (therapist's offices), and at specific times (sessions.)

4. Whatever is communicated during "psychotherapy" is to be kept confidential, with certain exceptions, which are clearly defined in laws/ethical standards.

Recovery-oriented treatment presents some challenges to these assumptions. For example, when the clinician is encouraged to do "whatever it takes" to promote recovery, much of the help looks nothing like traditional psychotherapy. Recovery is a cyclical, collaborative process that is not restricted to official sessions and treatment plans. And who is the expert in the new paradigm that puts the consumer in charge and flattens the hierarchy? In recovery-oriented settings, traditional notions of confidentiality are challenged and multiple relationships are almost inevitable.

What follows is the actual text of selected laws and ethical standards for your reference. They are organized into three categories: Scope of Practice, Confidentiality, and Dual or Multiple Relationships.

Note that this is not a comprehensive selection, since the emphasis is on laws/ethics for California MFTs. There may be some significant differences for LCSWs, LPCCs or other mental health professionals.

The reader should not rely on this document for legal advice. Indeed, there are no definitive authorities for the many legal/ethical dilemmas arising out of the new paradigm. Interpretations of laws and ethical standards are "under construction." The BBS acknowledges this transitional process when it says graduate coursework must include "the current leg., al patterns and trends in the mental health professions," and "differences in legal and ethical standards for different types of work settings" (B&P Code 4980.36(d)(2)(J)). Clearly, all of us—students, educators, clinicians, supervisors, consumers—must be part of the discussion and evolution of standards for recovery-oriented care.

I. What is "Psychotherapy?" Scope of practice for LMFTs, LCSWs, LPCCs and Clinical Psychologists

California law defines the practice of marriage and family therapy without actually using the term "psychotherapy," although the phrase "psychotherapeutic techniques" appears:

B&PC 4980.02: For the purposes of this chapter, the **practice of marriage and family therapy** shall mean that service performed with individuals, couples, or groups wherein interpersonal relationships are examined for the purpose of achieving more adequate, satisfying, and productive marriage and family adjustments. This practice includes relationship and pre-marriage counseling.

The application of marriage and family therapy principles and methods includes, but is not limited to, the use of applied psychotherapeutic techniques, to enable individuals to mature and grow within marriage and the family, the provision of explanations and interpretations of the psychosexual and psychosocial aspects of relationships, and the use, application, and integration of the coursework and training required by Sections **4980.37**, **4980**.40, and **4980**.41. (*These sections are the educational requirements for the license, including coursework in assessment and diagnosis of mental disorders, psychopharmacology, and psychological testing. The numbers may be changing as a result of SB 33 and the curriculum changes it mandates as of 2012)*

For comparative purposes, we include here the laws defining the scope of practice for social workers, professional clinical counselors, and clinical psychologists in California. These laws include extensive but not very useful definitions of "psychotherapy" and "applied psychotherapeutic techniques":

B&PC Code 4996.9: The **practice of clinical social work** is defined as a service in which a special knowledge of social resources, human capabilities, and the part that unconscious motivation plays in determining behavior, is directed at helping people to achieve more adequate, satisfying, and productive social adjustments. The application of social work principles and methods includes,

but is not restricted to, counseling and using applied psychotherapy of a nonmedical nature with individuals, families, or groups; providing information and referral services; providing or arranging for the provision of social services; explaining or interpreting the psychosocial aspects in the situations of individuals, families, or groups; helping communities to organize, to provide, or to improve social or health services; or doing research related to social work.

Psychotherapy, within the meaning of this chapter, is the use of psychosocial methods within a professional relationship, to assist the person or persons to achieve a better psychosocial adaptation, to acquire greater human realization of psychosocial potential and adaptation, to modify internal and external conditions which affect individuals, groups, or communities in respect to behavior, emotions, and thinking, in respect to their intrapersonal and interpersonal processes.

B&PC Code 2903: The **practice of psychology** is defined as rendering or offering to render for a fee to individuals, groups, organizations or the public any psychological service involving the application of psychological principles, methods, and procedures of understanding, predicting, and influencing behavior, such as the principles pertaining to learning, perception, motivation, emotions, and interpersonal relationships; and the methods and procedures of interviewing, counseling, psychotherapy, behavior modification, and hypnosis; and of constructing, administering, and interpreting tests of mental abilities, aptitudes, interests, attitudes, personality characteristics, emotions, and motivations.

The application of such principles and methods includes, but is not restricted to: diagnosis, prevention, treatment, and amelioration of psychological problems and emotional and mental disorders of individuals and groups.

Psychotherapy within the meaning of this chapter means the use of psychological methods in a professional relationship to assist a person or persons to acquire greater human effectiveness or to modify feelings, conditions, attitudes and behavior which are emotionally, intellectually, or socially ineffectual or maladjustive.

B&PC Code 4999.20. (a) (1) "**Professional clinical counseling**" means the application of counseling interventions and psychotherapeutic techniques to identify and remediate cognitive, mental, and emotional issues, including personal growth, adjustment to disability, crisis intervention, and psychosocial and environmental problems. Professional clinical counseling" includes conducting assessments for the purpose of establishing counseling goals and objectives to empower individuals to deal adequately with life situations, reduce stress, experience growth, change behavior, and make well-informed, rational decisions.

(2) "Professional clinical counseling" is focused exclusively on the application of counseling interventions and psychotherapeutic techniques for the purposes of improving mental health, and is not intended to capture other, nonclinical forms of counseling for the purposes of licensure. For purposes of this paragraph, "nonclinical" means non-mental health.

(3) "Professional clinical counseling" does not include the assessment or treatment of couples or families unless the professional clinical counselor has completed all of the following additional training and education, beyond the minimum training and education required for licensure:

(A) One of the following:

(i) Six semester units or nine quarter units specifically focused on the theory and application of marriage and family therapy.

(ii) A named specialization or emphasis area on the qualifying degree in marriage and family therapy; marital and family therapy; marriage, family, and child counseling; or couple and family therapy.

(B) No less than 500 hours of documented supervised experience working directly with couples, families, or children.

(C) A minimum of six hours of continuing education specific to marriage and family therapy, completed in each license renewal cycle.

(4) "Professional clinical counseling" does not include the provision of clinical social work services.

(b) "Counseling interventions and psychotherapeutic techniques" means the application of cognitive, affective, verbal or nonverbal, systemic or holistic counseling strategies that include principles of development, wellness, and maladjustment that reflect a pluralistic society. These interventions and techniques are specifically implemented in the context of a professional clinical counseling relationship and use a variety of counseling theories and approaches.

(c) "Assessment" means selecting, administering, scoring, and interpreting tests, instruments, and other tools and methods designed to measure an individual's attitudes, abilities, aptitudes, achievements, interests, personal characteristics, disabilities, and mental, emotional, and behavioral concerns and development and the use of methods and techniques for understanding human behavior in relation to coping with, adapting to, or ameliorating changing life situations, as part of the counseling process. "Assessment" shall not include the use of projective techniques in the

assessment of personality, individually administered intelligence tests, neuropsychological testing, or utilization of a battery of three or more tests to determine the presence of psychosis, dementia, amnesia, cognitive impairment, or criminal behavior.

For marriage and family therapy interns and trainees, hours of "client centered advocacy" may be counted as direct handling experience, therefore clearly within scope of practice. But what is "Client-Centered Advocacy?"

B&PC Code 4980.43(h) says: Client centered advocacy includes, but is not limited to, researching, identifying, and accessing resources, or other activities, related to obtaining or providing services and supports for clients or groups of clients receiving psychotherapy or counseling services.

II. Dual/multiple relationships:

In recovery-oriented care, roles and relationships often overlap. For example, consumers may be encouraged to help peers by functioning like clinicians, and clinicians often function like peers or friends in activities with consumers. While everyone is clear that sexual relationships are forbidden, there is less clarity about other multiple roles or role conflicts.

Relevant Codes for LMFTs

From AAMFT: 1.3 Marriage and family therapists are aware of their influential positions with respect to clients, and they avoid exploiting the trust and dependency of such persons. Therapists, therefore, make every effort to avoid conditions and multiple relationships with clients that could impair professional judgment or increase the risk of exploitation. Such relationships include, but are not limited to, business or close personal relationships with a client or the client's immediate family. When the risk of impairment or exploitation exists due to conditions or multiple roles, therapists take appropriate precautions.

1.4 Sexual intimacy with clients is prohibited.

1.5 Sexual intimacy with former clients is likely to be harmful and is therefore prohibited for two years following the termination of therapy or last professional contact. In an effort to avoid exploiting the trust and dependency of clients, marriage and family therapists should not engage in sexual intimacy with former clients after the two years following termination or last professional contact. Should therapists engage in sexual intimacy with former clients following two years after termination or last professional contact, the burden shifts to the therapist to demonstrate that there has been no exploitation or injury to the former client or to the client's immediate family.

3.4 Marriage and family therapists do not provide services that create a conflict of interest that may impair work performance or clinical judgment.

From CAMFT: 1.2 Marriage and family therapists are aware of their influential position with respect to patients, and they avoid exploiting the trust and dependency of such persons. Marriage and family therapists therefore avoid dual relationshipsiv that are reasonably likely to impair professional judgment or lead to exploitation. A dual relationship occurs when a therapist and his/her patient engage in a separate and distinct relationship either simultaneously with the therapeutic relationship, or during a reasonable period of time following the termination of the therapeutic relationship. Not all dual relationships are unethical, and some dual relationships cannot be avoided. When a dual relationship cannot be avoided, therapists take appropriate professional precautions to insure that judgment is not impaired and that no exploitation occurs.

1.2.1 Sexual intercourse, sexual contact or sexual intimacy with a patient, or a patient's spouse or partner, during the therapeutic relationship, or during the two years following the termination of the therapeutic relationship, is unethical.

1.2.2 Other acts which would result in unethical dual relationships include, but are not limited to borrowing money from a patient, hiring a patient, engaging in a business venture with a patient, or engaging in a close personal relationship with a patient. Such acts with a patient's spouse, partner or family member may also be considered unethical dual relationships.

1.2.3 Marriage and family therapists do not enter into therapeutic relationships with persons with whom they have had a sexual relationship.

1.16 NON-THERAPIST ROLES: When marriage and family therapists engage in professional roles other than treatment or supervision (including, but not limited to, managed care utilization review, consultation, coaching, adoption service, or behavior analysis), they act solely within that role and clarify, when necessary to avoid confusion with consumers and employers, how that role is distinguished from the practice of marriage and family therapy.

Relevant Codes for LCSWs

NASW 1.06 Conflicts of Interest (a) Social workers should be alert to and avoid conflicts of interest that interfere with the exercise of professional discretion and impartial judgment. Social workers should inform clients when a real or potential conflict of interest arises and take reasonable steps to resolve the issue in a manner that makes the clients' interests primary and protects clients' interests to the greatest extent possible. In some cases, protecting clients' interests may require termination

of the professional relationship with proper referral of the client...(b) Social workers should not take unfair advantage of any professional relationship or exploit others to further their personal, religious, political, or business interests. (c) Social workers should not engage in dual or multiple relationships with clients or former clients in which there is a risk of exploitation or potential harm to the client. In instances when dual or multiple relationships are unavoidable, social workers should take steps to protect clients and are responsible for setting clear, appropriate, and culturally sensitive boundaries. (Dual or multiple relationships occur when social workers relate to clients in more than one relationship, whether professional, social, or business. Dual or multiple relationships can occur simultaneously or consecutively.)

(b) Social workers should not engage in sexual activities or sexual contact with clients' relatives or other individuals with whom clients maintain a close personal relationship when there is a risk of exploitation or potential harm to the client. Sexual activity or sexual contact with clients' relatives or other individuals with whom clients maintain a personal relationship has the potential to be harmful to the client and may make it difficult for the social worker and client to maintain appropriate professional boundaries. Social workers—not their clients, their clients' relatives, or other individuals with whom the client maintains a personal relationship—assume the full burden for setting clear, appropriate, and culturally sensitive boundaries.

I. Social workers should not engage in sexual activities or sexual contact with former clients because of the potential for harm to the client. If social workers engage in conduct contrary to this prohibition or claim that an exception to this prohibition is warranted because of extraordinary circumstances, it is social workers—not their clients—who assume the full burden of demonstrating that the former client has not been exploited, coerced, or manipulated, intentionally or unintentionally.

(d) Social workers should not provide clinical services to individuals with whom they have had a prior sexual relationship. Providing clinical services to a former sexual partner has the potential to be harmful to the individual and is likely to make it difficult for the social worker and individual to maintain appropriate professional boundaries.

NASW 1.10 Physical Contact: Social workers should not engage in physical contact with clients when there is a possibility of psychological harm to the client as a result of the contact (such as cradling or caressing clients). Social workers who engage in appropriate physical contact with clients are responsible for setting clear, appropriate, and culturally sensitive boundaries that govern such physical contact.

Relevant Codes for LPCCs:

From the American Counseling Association (ACA)

A.5.a. Current Clients: Sexual or romantic counselor–client interactions or relationships with current clients, their romantic partners, or their family members are prohibited.

A.5.b. Former Clients: Sexual or romantic counselor–client interactions or relationships with former clients, their romantic partners, or their family members are prohibited for a period of 5 years following the last professional contact. Counselors, before engaging in sexual or romantic interactions or relationships with clients, their romantic partners, or client family members after 5 years following the last professional contact, demonstrate forethought and document (in written form) whether the interactions or relationship can be viewed as exploitive in some way and/or whether there is still potential to harm the former client; in cases of potential exploitation and/or harm, the counselor avoids entering such an interaction or relationship.

A.5.c. Nonprofessional Interactions or Relationships (Other Than Sexual or Romantic Interactions or Relationships): Counselor–client nonprofessional relationships with clients, former clients, their romantic partners, or their family members should be avoided, except when the interaction is potentially beneficial to the client. (See A.5.d.)

A.5.d. Potentially Beneficial Interactions: When a counselor–client nonprofessional interaction with a client or former client may be potentially beneficial to the client or former client, the counselor must document in case records, prior to the interaction (when feasible), the rationale for such an interaction, the potential benefit, and anticipated consequences for the client or former client and other individuals significantly involved with the client or former client. Such interactions should be initiated with appropriate client consent. Where unintentional harm occurs to the client or former client, or to an individual significantly involved with the client or former client, due to the nonprofessional interaction, the counselor must show evidence of an attempt to remedy such harm. Examples of potentially beneficial interactions include, but are not limited to, attending a formal ceremony (e.g., a wedding/commitment ceremony or graduation); purchasing a service or product provided by a client or former client (excepting unrestricted bartering); hospital visits to an ill family member; mutual membership in a professional association, organization, or community. (See A.5.c.)

A.5.e. Role Changes in the Professional Relationship: When a counselor changes a role from the original or most recent contracted relationship, he or she obtains informed consent from the client and explains the right of the client to refuse services related to the change. Examples of role changes include: 1) changing from individual to relationship or family counseling, or vice versa; 2)

changing from a non-forensic evaluative role to a therapeutic role, or vice versa; 3) changing from a counselor to a researcher role (i.e., enlisting clients as research participants), or vice versa; and 4) changing from a counselor to a mediator role, or vice versa.

Clients must be fully informed of any anticipated consequences (e.g., financial, legal, personal, or therapeutic) of counselor role changes.

III. Confidentiality

Laws/ethical standards regarding confidentiality assume an environment where psychotherapy occurs only in offices with closed doors, separated from the flow of everyday life. In recovery-oriented treatment settings, communication between clinician and consumer is often much less structured, and privacy is neither possible nor expected. How shall we adapt/interpret the existing standards? Are new standards required?

From CAMFT: Marriage and family therapists have unique confidentiality responsibilities because the "patient" in a therapeutic relationship may be more than one person. The overriding principle is that marriage and family therapists respect the confidences of their patient(s).

2.1 DISCLOSURES OF CONFIDENTIAL INFORMATION: Marriage and family therapists do not disclose patient confidences, including the names or identities of their patients, to anyone except a) as mandated by law b) as permitted by law c) when the marriage and family therapist is a defendant in a civil, criminal, or disciplinary action arising from the therapy (in which case patient confidences may only be disclosed in the course of that action), or d) if there is an authorization previously obtained in writing, and then such information may only be revealed in accordance with the terms of the authorization.

2.2 SIGNED AUTHORIZATIONS—RELEASE OF INFORMATION: When there is a request for information related to any aspect of psychotherapy or treatment, each member of the unit receiving such therapeutic treatment must sign an authorization before a marriage and family therapist will disclose information received from any member of the treatment unit.

2.3 ELECTRONIC MEDIA: Marriage and family therapists are aware of the possible adverse effects of technological changes with respect to the dissemination of patient information, and take care when disclosing such information. Marriage and family therapists are also aware of the limitations regarding confidential transmission by Internet or electronic media and take care when transmitting or receiving such information via these mediums.

2.4 MAINTENANCE OF PATIENT RECORDS—CONFIDENTIALITY: Marriage and family therapists store, transfer, transmit, and/or dispose of patient records in ways that protect confidentiality.

2.5 EMPLOYEES—CONFIDENTIALITY: Marriage and family therapists take appropriate steps to ensure, insofar as possible, that the confidentiality of patients is maintained by their employees, supervisees, assistants, and volunteers.

2.6 USE OF CLINICAL MATERIALS—CONFIDENTIALITY: Marriage and family therapists use clinical materials in teaching, writing, and public presentations only if a written authorization has been previously obtained in accordance with 2.1 d), or when appropriate steps have been taken to protect patient identity.

2.7 GROUPS—CONFIDENTIALITY: Marriage and family therapists, when working with a group, educate the group regarding the importance of maintaining confidentiality, and are encouraged to obtain written agreement from group participants to respect the confidentiality of other members of the group.

From AAMFT: 2.2 Marriage and family therapists do not disclose client confidences except by written authorization or waiver, or where mandated or permitted by law. Verbal authorization will not be sufficient except in emergency situations, unless prohibited by law. When providing couple, family or group treatment, the therapist does not disclose information outside the treatment context without a written authorization from each individual competent to execute a waiver. In the context of couple, family or group treatment, the therapist may not reveal any individual's confidences to others in the client unit without the prior written permission of that individual.

2.6 Marriage and family therapists, when consulting with colleagues or referral sources, do not share confidential information that could reasonably lead to the identification of a client, research participant, supervisee, or other person with whom they have a confidential relationship unless they have obtained the prior written consent of the client, research participant, supervisee, or other person with whom they have a confidential relationship. Information may be shared only to the extent necessary to achieve the purposes of the consultation.

Relevant Codes for Social Workers (From NASW)

NASW 1.07 Privacy and Confidentiality: (a) Social workers should respect clients' right to privacy. Social workers should not solicit private information from clients unless it is essential to providing services or conducting social work evaluation or research. Once private information is shared, standards of confidentiality apply.

(b) Social workers may disclose confidential information when appropriate with valid consent from a client or a person legally authorized to consent on behalf of a client.

Social workers should protect the confidentiality of all information obtained in the course of professional service, except for compelling professional reasons. The general expectation that social workers will keep information confidential does not apply when disclosure is necessary to prevent serious, foreseeable, and imminent harm to a client or other identifiable person. In all instances, social workers should disclose the least amount of confidential information necessary to achieve the desired purpose; only information that is directly relevant to the purpose for which the disclosure is made should be revealed.

(d) Social workers should inform clients, to the extent possible, about the disclosure of confidential information and the potential consequences, when feasible before the disclosure is made. This applies whether social workers disclose confidential information on the basis of a legal requirement or client consent.

(e) Social workers should discuss with clients and other interested parties the nature of confidentiality and limitations of clients' right to confidentiality. Social workers should review with clients circumstances where confidential information may be requested and where disclosure of confidential information may be legally required. This discussion should occur as soon as possible in the social workerclient relationship and as needed throughout the course of the relationship.

(f) When social workers provide counseling services to families, couples, or groups, social workers should seek agreement among the parties involved concerning each individual's right to confidentiality and obligation to preserve the confidentiality of information shared by others. Social workers should inform participants in family, couples, or group counseling that social workers cannot guarantee that all participants will honor such agreements.

(g) Social workers should inform clients involved in family, couples, marital, or group counseling of the social worker's, employer's, and agency's policy concerning the social worker's disclosure of confidential information among the parties involved in the counseling.

(h) Social workers should not disclose confidential information to thirdparty payers unless clients have authorized such disclosure.

(i) Social workers should not discuss confidential information in any setting unless privacy can be ensured. Social workers should not discuss confidential information in public or semipublic areas such as hallways, waiting rooms, elevators, and restaurants.

(p) Social workers should not disclose identifying information when discussing clients for teaching or training purposes unless the client has consented to disclosure of confidential information.

(q) Social workers should not disclose identifying information when discussing clients with consultants unless the client has consented to disclosure of confidential information or there is a compelling need for such disclosure.

Relevant Codes for LPCCs

From ACA: Counselors recognize that trust is a cornerstone of the counseling relationship. Counselors aspire to earn the trust of clients by creating an ongoing partnership, establishing and upholding appropriate boundaries, and maintaining confidentiality. Counselors communicate the parameters of confidentiality in a culturally competent manner.

B.1. Respecting Client Rights

B.1.a. Multicultural/Diversity Considerations: Counselors maintain awareness and sensitivity regarding cultural meanings of confidentiality and privacy. Counselors respect differing views toward disclosure of information. Counselors hold ongoing discussions with clients as to how, when, and with whom information is to be shared.

B.1.b. Respect for Privacy: Counselors respect client rights to privacy. Counselors solicit private information from clients only when it is beneficial to the counseling process.

B.1.c. Respect for Confidentiality: Counselors do not share confidential information without client consent or without sound legal or ethical justification.

B.1.d. Explanation of Limitations: At initiation and throughout the counseling process, counselors inform clients of the limitations of confidentiality and seek to identify foreseeable situations in which confidentiality must be breached. (See A.2.b.)

B.3.b. Treatment Teams: When client treatment involves a continued review or participation by a treatment team, the client will be informed of the team's existence and composition, information being shared, and the purposes of sharing such information.

B.3.c. Confidential Settings: Counselors discuss confidential information only in settings in which they can reasonably ensure client privacy....

B.3.e. Transmitting Confidential Information: Counselors take precautions to ensure the confidentiality of information transmitted through the use of computers, electronic mail, facsimile machines, telephones, voicemail, answering machines, and other electronic or computer technology. (See A.12.g.)

B.4. Groups and Families B.4.a. Group Work In group work, counselors clearly explain the importance and parameters of confidentiality for the specific group being entered.

B.4.b. Couples and Family Counseling: In couples and family counseling, counselors clearly define who is considered "the client" and discuss expectations and limitations of confidentiality. Counselors seek agreement and document in writing such agreement among all involved parties having capacity to give consent concerning each individual's right to confidentiality and any obligation to preserve the confidentiality of information known.

B.5.c. Release of Confidential Information: When counseling minor clients or adult clients who lack the capacity to give voluntary consent to release confidential information, counselors seek permission from an appropriate third party to disclose information. In such instances, counselors inform clients consistent with their level of understanding and take culturally appropriate measures to safeguard client confidentiality....

B.6.a. Confidentiality of Records: Counselors ensure that records are kept in a secure location and that only authorized persons have access to records.

B.6.b. Permission to Record: Counselors obtain permission from clients prior to recording sessions through electronic or other means.

B.6.c. Permission to Observe: Counselors obtain permission from clients prior to observing counseling sessions, reviewing session transcripts, or viewing recordings of sessions with supervisors, faculty, peers, or others within the training environment.

CALIFORNIA LAWS RELEVANT TO DUAL RELATIONSHIPS AND CONFIDENTIALITY

While each profession has its own ethical standards, California law contains several codes relevant to scope of practice, confidentiality and dual relationships. These laws apply to all licensees or registrants with the Board of Behavioral Sciences.

Unprofessional Conduct

B&PC 4982 (Denial, Suspension, Revocation, Grounds)

The Board may refuse to issue an intern registration or a license or may suspend or revoke the license or intern registration of any registrant or licensee if the applicant, licensee, or registrant has been guilty of unprofessional conduct. Unprofessional conduct shall include, but not be limited to:

(k) Engaging in sexual relations with a client, soliciting sexual relations or committing an act of sexual abuse or sexual misconduct with a client, an act punishable as a sexually related crime, if that act or solicitation is related to the qualifications, functions or duties of a marriage and family therapist.

(l) Performing, or holding one's self out as being able to perform, or offering to perform or permitting, any trainee or intern under supervision to perform any professional services beyond the scope of the license authorized by this chapter.

(m) Failure to maintain confidentiality, except as otherwise required or permitted by law, of all information that has been received from a client in confidence during the course of treatment and all information about the client which is obtained from tests or other means.

THE PARALLEL PROCESS: PARALLEL PROCESS AND THE RECOVERY MODEL

Margaret L. Avineri, Psy.D.

As one would imagine, the incorporation of Recovery-oriented principles into treatment and therapeutic intervention necessitates a re-training and re-orienting of clinical supervisors who are charged with implementing this shift. The likelihood is that this altered approach will express itself both in the content of the supervision and the process of mentoring clinicians in training. The most intriguing area where we can observe this transformation in action is in the "Parallel Process."

The concept of Parallel Process evolved from the psychoanalytic phenomena of transference and counter-transference where feelings, beliefs or attitudes manifest in the therapeutic relationship and work of therapist and patient. This "parallel process" was later observed in the one-on-one dynamics of supervising clinicians in their work with clients. Searles (1955) extended the idea of parallel process in suggesting that "processes at work currently in the relationship between patient and therapist are often reflected in the relationship between therapist and supervisor."

Today, as we incorporate principles of The Recovery Model in clinical supervision, parallel process takes on an expanded meaning and new level of complexity. The inherent hierarchical structure and power differentials in agency and public mental health settings (e.g. funder, agency, directors, supervisors, clinicians and Interns) present a unique challenge to the philosophy espoused by the Recovery-oriented approach. The traditional role of supervisor as "expert" is called into question as we venture into an uncharted dynamic in which every participant's input is valued equally and incorporated into decision-making. Under the new collaborative paradigm, supervisors are expected to integrate recovery principles and practice into supervision to literally provide a recovery-oriented experience for supervisees.

Just as the therapeutic relationship empowers the consumer to direct his recovery, so supervisors are invited to alter their approach to supervision and training to become one in which the clinician charts his own professional development. Supervision, therefore, in order to effectively demonstrate and "live" recovery principles, should provide a parallel experience for the clinician. Supervisees will not only turn to supervisors for training, guidance and answers but also freely share their own ideas and impressions in planning and implementing treatment. The interaction with supervisors will reflect a new respect for and elevation of the clinician's ideas, hopes and experience, to have equal footing with the supervisors' knowledge, creating an even playing field for every level of input. This will undoubtedly create multiple dilemmas and conflicts for the agency and staff who must fulfill

their obligations to funders and stakeholders (and manage risk) while actively shifting the way they do business. The goal is to create a multi-dimensional learning experience for everyone involved. The underlying assumption is that this shift in methodology will facilitate the clinician's capacity to work more successfully and collaboratively with consumers.

References

Searles, H.F. (1955). The informational value of the supervisor's emotional experience. *Psychiatry*, 5(18), pp. 135-146.

Sumerel, M.B. (1994), *Parallel process in supervision*. Greensboro, NC: Eric Digest.

PARALLEL PROCESS IN SUPERVISION

Mary M. Read, Ph.D.

Learning to distinguish process from content is one of the more challenging tasks for counselors in training. The richness of process (e.g., in terms of access to emotions and awareness of motivations) makes it a crucial tool in both therapy and the development of the therapist. Because it highlights similar dynamics taking place in the therapy setting and the supervision context, focusing on the phenomenon of parallel process can be an aid to developing a 'process awareness' during supervision, making it a richer experience for all. Following is an example taken from a practicum class a few years ago.

An MFT trainee came into group supervision bringing concerns about a case. The client, a middle-aged woman, was experiencing conflict with her young adult child, which the client described in a very judgmental, almost angry tone. As the trainee, a woman in her late 20's, spoke about her client, her tone was also judgmental (of her client) and almost angry as she detailed how she had tried to intervene with her client, to no apparent avail. The supervisor asked the trainee what the client might be feeling, in order to be coming across as angry and judgmental. When the trainee could offer no insight, the group helped her process to see that the client was likely fearful of losing the relationship with her child, feeling inadequate to the task of parenting a (now) adult child, and unsure as to how to proceed in a beneficial manner.

Dropping into immediacy to highlight the dynamic that was "live in the room" during supervision, the supervisor then asked how the supervisee was feeling about the case. The trainee admitted she felt like she had no control over the client feeling better, wasn't sure how to be of help, and was afraid she might not be "doing it right". Facing her own fear that she might not be "enough" for the client helped the trainee identify with her client's fears in her relationship with her child. The supervisor reflected that these feelings of fear and inadequacy often tend to spark a judgmental response, in an attempt to restore the illusion of control.

The trainee could see that her own response to her client was nearly identical to the response of her client to the client's child. In both cases, fear of inadequacy/losing the relationship was coloring the tone of interaction, producing judgment. When judgment is met with compassion it naturally lifts, so as the trainee lifted her judgment of the client by finding compassion and empathy for her, she could take what was modeled for her in supervision back into the clinical setting and replicate that response with her client.

This is parallel process in action. What was going on in session with the client was being reproduced in group supervision, where it could be worked with directly because the emotional content was "live" for the trainee (vs. reporting what a client might be feeling, which will not "move" in the same way). The same thing that helped the trainee feel better (lifting the judgment, facing the fear, allowing compassion) will then likely help the client as well, since it's the same issue and the trainee has experienced help, not just learned about it.

THᴴ

PART THREE

FROM THE CLASSROOM TO THE REAL WORLD: WHAT DO YOU NEED TO KNOW?

- Direct from the Employers

- Direct from the Consumers

- Preparing for the Future

DIRECT FROM THE EMPLOYERS

In the following section, employers representing a diversity of work settings "speak" to you. We contacted a diversity of community agencies in the California public mental health system and asked their top management to help us educate you to be prepared to work for them. We asked them what matters to them and what makes a difference when they interview applicants for placement or employment positions.

The following pages contain the unedited responses that we received. You will find some general information along with guidance related specifically to your increased marketability in a recovery-oriented health care setting. The agencies listed below graciously responded to our request for guidance for you:

- Bonita House: http://www.bonitahouse.org

- Casa Pacifica: http://www.casapacifica.org

- Child and Family Center, Santa Clarita: http://www.childfamilycenter.org

- Didi Hirsch Mental Health Services: http://www.didihirsch.org

- Foothill Family Service: http://www.foothillfamily.org

- Jewish Family Service of Los Angeles: http://www.jfsla.org

- L.A. County Department of Mental Health: http://dmh.lacounty.gov/wps/portal/dmh

- Sanctuary Psychiatric Centers of Santa Barbara: http://www.spcsb.org

- Turning Point of Central California: http://www.tpocc.org

MFT ACADEMIC TRAINING WISH LIST FOR WORKING IN PUBLIC MENTAL HEALTH

Rick Crispino, Executive Director

Familiarity with:

- Psychopharmacology

- Understanding of the major psychiatric diagnoses

- Substance abuse coursework

- Minkoff Quadrant Model

- Understanding of SAMHSA Evidence Based Practices

- Understanding that recovery is possible

- Use of hopeful and respectful language; person first language

- Community based settings beyond clinic based settings

- NAMI support groups and 12 Step Meetings

- How to work with people who are suicidal

- Trauma Informed Treatment

- Dialectical Behavioral Treatment

- Stages of Change

- Documentation training to be able to pass Federal and State compliance audits

- Consumers of public mental health services and their family members

What We Look For In Clinicians

1. What do you look for in PMH?

2. Is it attitude? Experience? Courses taken? Specific skills?

3. What do you want them to not worry about because you would rather train them "on the job"?

4. How can they best prepare themselves to be of value to you and fit in with your work setting and culture?

Kinds of people:

1. We want people who are committed to (passionate about/interested in) working communities (vs. people more oriented toward solely working as private practitioners).

2. We want people who are interested in working as part of multi-disciplinarian teams (and who do not have professional preciousness).

3. We want people who value research and science as a foundation to our work.

4. We want people who want to learn more and who are willing to take risks in their own growth.

5. We want people who will CONSULT, CONSULT, CONSULT with their supervisors!

6. We want people who like people (RELATIONSHIP oriented).

7. We want people who appreciate and respect diversity.

8. We want people who have solid boundaries and a clear understanding of professionalism.

Knowledge Base:

- Basic understanding of psychopathology (can use a DSM).

- Basic understanding of legal/ethical issues (have taken at LEAST one course in that area).

- Basic understanding of various theoretical orientations (esp. CBT).

- Basic understanding of domains of diversity

- Basic understanding of public mental health system.

- Basic understanding of how mental health issues are dealt with in school systems. Understanding how the language used in Individualized Education Plans (IEPs) differs from concepts and language used in mental health practice and MTP goals.

- Basic understanding of and appreciation for value of "self-help", client voice and choice, and professional skills.

- Basic understanding of modes of service delivery – "writing" vs. "seeking" mode.

Skill Base:

- Can write.

- Can conduct initial intakes/evaluations (have had SOME experience – don't need tons).

- Computer literate.

- Documentation skills are helpful.

- We are happy to provide OJT in every aspect of our various positions here.

- Prepare self by being willing to integrate and apply what you are learning in grad school with what we are doing in the community, practicing basic skill set, reading up on us. Don't come to an interview or position without having read our web page and without having googled us, and knowing basics for crisis work.

- Strong communication skills.

- Customer Service orientation.

"Employer Wish List"

I. What do we look for?

- Experience (either in a classroom setting or in vivo) working with adults who have severe mental illnesses and children and their families who struggle with severe emotional disturbances

- Willingness to work in the field (e.g., clients' homes, schools, board and care and other community locations)

- Ability to link client presentation, presenting problem, and reported symptoms and behaviors with diagnostic categories in the DSM-IV

- Knowledge of the Recovery Principles. In other words, viewing clinical work as a collaborative process with the client, starting from client strengths and letting go of preconceived notions about client's mental health trajectory.

- Ability to understand and work with other systems (e.g., medical, family, school, justice) involved in a client's life.

- Excellent written and verbal communication skills

- Desire for constant learning and not viewing self as expert which entails collaborating with the client, other professionals, and the system.

- Being able to handle uncertainty and not always having the "right" answer

- Self-reflection, emotional maturity, ability to cope with anxiety and change. Recognize that change in community mental health is constant so flexibility and adaptability is necessary.

II. What we will train in "on the job"

- Field safety

- Case management

- Documentation

Larry Schallert: Director of Adult, Education and Outreach Services, Child & Family Center Santa Clarita
Roberta Rubin: Clinical Services Director

What do Employers Look for:

Graduate students need to know that employers are looking at work habits. They are wanting to see a good positive attitude and they want interviewees to be able to demonstrate knowledge they have gained from previous employment, internships and studies. They want them to be personable in the interview and be able to hold a conversation. We evaluate their ability to answer "what they would do" scenarios. We look for common sense and an ability to know what they know and most importantly what they don't know and how they would find out. We want them to know to consult with their supervisor and when.

In addition we look to see that they are dressed professionally. We look to see that they only share appropriate information for the job and it is a really bad sign if we get "too much info" about their private life or talk negatively about previous supervisors. In the community mental health setting for children we like them to have at least a year treating emotionally disturbed children/adolescents and have some family therapy experience. They should like working with families and be eager to work in the community such as schools and homes when necessary. Similarly, we would want them to have at least a year treating and/or working with adults with serious and persistent mental illness or serious emotional difficulties.

If students or applicants have the above characteristics they can learn on the job and shouldn't worry about knowing Electronic Health Records Systems, specific evidence-based programs, how to treat rare or difficult situations, and leg., al and ethically dilemmas. However if they have some familiarity or experience with those items and/or know DMH paperwork it will go a long way in the interview. Other items that would be helpful to have an understanding of and be able to share experience with would be the Recovery Model, Milestones to Recovery, Wellness Centers, the public community mental health system, co-occurring disorders, Medical Necessity, NAMI, Regional Center and the world of the developmentally disabled, especially as it relates to those with DD and emotional

problems or mental illness, special education and schools, HIPAA, and cultural competency issues.

Obviously, having the ability to read, write and converse fluently in a language such as Spanish, Korean, Russian, Farsi, Armenian etc. is a major plus and often we will hire a person with less experience who has the personal attributes listed above, if they have an important language skill. Increasingly important is the skills to work with health providers and knowledge of the health system and how health and mental health are linked. Finally, any experience working, linking and/or collaborating with public county departments such as probation, mental health, DCFS, Public Health, Health Sheriff and Police, the VA, PMRT etc. is a plus. A person who can work in the community and with the community and knows the resources is a valuable employee who can understand the world of families with mental health needs.

"Employer Wish List"

When candidates come to us with very little work experience because they are right out of school, we really look for the following experience and qualities (candidates with these qualities that we have hired have turned out to be great):

- Flexible, adaptable and team oriented. PMH is not for people who want boring, predictable jobs!

- Commitment to serve and give back to the community. PMH is not for people who just want a job and a salary, but for people with a heart for serving the low-economic, culturally diverse communities.

- Community-based work experience and exposure to seeing clients in non-traditional settings

- Experience working with at-risk populations and SED kids

- A "can-do" attitude and ability to demonstrate going above and beyond is usually more valuable than actual work experience as we can provide training for documentation, EBPs, EHRS, etc., but we have not been too successful in training people to have a "can-do" attitude or the desire to go beyond their defined work.

- Very creative quick thinkers and learners – must be able to think on their feet and think outside the box. Our clients are not text-book clients and they often having life circumstances far removed from the average American's experience so the PMH therapist must be able to adapt all they have learned in the classroom to fit very unique situations. Additionally, resources in PMH are often very limited so staff have to be able to do creative things without a lot of stuff to work with – this is actually great experience because they have to model the same for their clients – e.g. show a family living in a bad neighborhood and with no money for extra expenses how to use the materials they have on hand to create fun, family bonding activities to do inside their tiny apartment.

- Experience in diagnosis and use of the DSM

- DMH paperwork experience, experience/exposure to EBPs would be a plus

- Experience or exposure to documenting in an EHRS is also very helpful.

How students should prepare themselves: if they want to work in PMH, they really should seek out practicum experiences in this setting so they can get a sense for whether they will be a good fit for PMH (and will like it) as well as come to us with exposure to similar work setting and culture to what we have.

A family
of services.
A family
that serves.

What Jewish Family Service Looks for in Candidates for its DMH Programs

- Since applications to our programs are submitted online, the first thing we notice about a candidate is how s/he presents in writing. Specifically, we look at writing ability, attention to detail, and the ability to express him/herself clearly. In the resume, previous positions held should state the nature of the work done and the specific population worked with, not just the name of the agency where a practicum or job took place. This first look at a candidate's writing gives us an idea of what an individual's writing skill will be for progress notes, assessments, and other clinical paperwork.

- We seek out and appreciate cultural diversity and multiple language capacity both as a requirement for certain positions and an enhancement of our staffing. Whenever possible, we hire candidates who represent the backgrounds of the populations we serve.

- We look to see if a candidate's experience is relevant to the services we provide. If we are hiring for an older adult program, we will give priority to those who have already obtained experience working with an older adult population.

- Individuals should have a strong therapy background with a variety of cases before graduating to be ready for real-world clients. It is a plus when Practicum or previous work includes case management but we do look for good clinical experience in order for a clinician to be prepared for therapy work. In addition, we look for clinicians who have experience providing both long- and short-term therapy.

- During the interview, we look for individuals with a level of maturity and professionalism. Dress is important, as is the way candidates present themselves verbally. All aspects of the interview are relevant to the hiring process.

- The candidate should be able to discuss at least one case in depth, using clinical and theoretical terminology. Employers want to know that a candidate can conceptualize cases and have a coherent plan for treatment, rather than think that "anything goes" in

the treatment process.

- The tone a candidate sets in discussing clients during the interview is of utmost importance. Are clients spoken about with respect and as a collaborative part of the process, or is derogatory or belittling language used? We look for employees who will value clients, work collaboratively with them, and focus on their strengths.

- We look for candidates who are able to demonstrate effective time-management skills. There are many demands on clinicians working within the DMH system, and the individual must be able to meet those competing demands while providing quality care to clients.

- Candidates must be able to be flexible in their style. We look for a willingness to do home visits, as many of our programs provide services almost exclusively in the community. Working within a public mental health system includes understanding and working with changes that happen on an ongoing basis. Clinicians must be able to adapt to changing work requirements and learning new skills as required.

- Knowledge of both DMH paperwork and evidence-based practices (EBPs) are a plus, but we will hire and train the right person regardless of experience in either of these areas.

L.A. COUNTY DEPARTMENT OF MENTAL HEALTH

Excerpts from a Power Point Presentation to the MFT Consortium May 20, 2011
Robin Kay, Ph.D., Chief Deputy Director,
Los Angeles County Department of Mental Health

- Desirable qualities for MFTs delivering Tier 1 services (individuals with serious and persistent mental illnesses with a high need for mental health and rehabilitation interventions)

  » Embrace a recovery approach

  » Willingness to work with clients as partners on teams (service extender approach)

  » Genuine belief in client-centered care including clients as participants in their own treatment team

  » Desire to create a welcoming environment

  » Flexibility in service delivery regarding location, structure of treatment

  » Familiar with assessment and treatment of co-occurring disorders (mental health and substance abuse)

  » Ability to deliver evidence-based services for this population

    * Assertive community treatment

    * Case management

    * Psycho-education

    * Supportive housing, education, employment

- Desirable qualities for MFTs delivering Tier 2 services (individuals seen in medical settings with mental health issues with a moderate need for interventions)

  » Willingness to collaborate with primary care providers

  » Flexibility in approach ("warm hand-off")

  » Comfort working with an interdisciplinary team

  » Comfort with brief treatment models – and acceptance of parameters

  » Ability to form relationships consistent with the boundaries of short term treatment

» Ability to efficiently conduct a comprehensive assessment and arrive at a differential diagnosis

» Skill in delivery of early intervention/brief evidence-based practices – particularly those effective in primary care settings (MHIP – aka IMPACT)

» Ability to work with increasingly diverse ethnic and linguistic populations, understanding the translation of ebps for diverse groups

» Ability to efficiently tailor treatment plan to presenting problem and short term intervention

» Acceptance of importance of outcome evaluation

Sanctuary Psychiatric Centers of Santa Barbara

Lisa Moschini, Clinical Director

When Can You Start?

When I was a graduate student, and computers were as big as Cadillac's, I was just happy to have completed my thesis. The thought of skills that employers would want never even entered my mind. I listened to my professors and completed coursework and internships without question. Today, however things are very different and much of the onus for practicum sites and "job training" falls squarely upon the shoulders of the graduate. As such, your choices prior to and post-graduation can raise your resume to the top of the heap or just as easily sink it to the bottom of the pile.

Pre-Graduation: Where you choose to complete your traineeship and what you actually learn is not something to be taken lightly. Most people do not begin an internship in private practice but instead join a team of professionals working in a milieu setting. This environment is ripe for learning experiences if you know what to look for and subsequently ask the right questions.

DO...	DON'T...
Talk to other people in your program and ask them about their experiences at internship sites. Pick wisely.	Wait until the last minute to seek a practicum site and in the interview don't forget to look for what they can offer you.
Choose groups to co-lead with a variety of providers. You can learn a lot by watching other clinicians "styles".	Just watch the leaders, ask to lead a group (while they monitor) if it is not offered or isn't part of the training experience.
Choose groups that will round out your resume (verbal, non-verbal, process, psycho-educational). This offers a prospective employer a well-rounded candidate .	Forgo meeting with providers either after or before a group. It is integral to your training that you get feedback from providers as well as supervisors.
Request clients with a broad range of diagnosis' for your individual caseload (mood, thought, and addiction).	Ignore the importance of reviewing your progress notes in supervision. Learning to write a proper note is imperative.

DO...	DON'T...
Incorporate a multiplicity of theories with your clients. It is not good practice to only have experience with one theoretical modality.	Hesitate to vary your interventions once you have arrived at a theoretical modality for your client/s.
Know the expectations and requirements of the BBS both pre and post-graduation. Go to the BBS website for informational needs.	Rely upon your school or supervisor/s to provide relevant information reg., arding licensing.
Diversify your experiences	**Limit your experiences**

Post-graduation: The resume is all powerful at this juncture. Now is the time to synthesize your capabilities into a one (1) page recitation of many years of experience. If you have diversified your pre-graduate learning this should be a simple task, if you have not some creative writing may be in your future.

DO...	DON'T...
Follow the job listing requirements to the letter. If it instructs you to do something, even something miniscule, do it their way.	Take short cuts when resonding to a job listing. To do so indicates you will not listen to job task/ expectations if hired.
Pay attention to content. Include a cover letter and always use spell check, then read your resume out loud to make certain it flows.	List every class you have ever taken. In fact don't list any courses, you have a degree I can surmise you took the appropriate modules.
Attach your resume with a personalized cover letter to prospective employers.	Imbed your resume in the body of an email or send a "template" cover letter.
Review prospective employer's websites and literature.	Just read website content, search it and identify how you can complement the prospective employers program. Say that in the interview.
Submit a resume that is one page and a personalized cover letter that is ½ to one page long.	Submit a resume that is longer than one page unless you have been working for many years in the Mental Health field. Do your talking in the interview not in writing.
Send a thank you email or letter after the interview.	Call to say thank you after the interview.

In the end, no one can formulate all the skills necessary to integrate into a prevailing work culture. But you can prepare yourself to offer prospective employers something to enhance an existing program.

This is what I seek in a potential candidate:

- Where can they add strength to our weakness?

- What skills do they offer?

- Who are they and will their personalities fit within the team?

- Do they accept feedback and are they willing to learn?

Wally Parks, Regional Administrator
Turning Point of Central California, Inc.

I think that most graduates of MFT programs need to be prepared to demonstrate and articulate their ability to learn. I would also say a dose of social work, good old- fashioned case management experience and training is of value. This has added value to the clinician but also in ability to guide other staff (PSC, Rehab) in carrying out case management functions.

They need to be adept at managing time to complete paperwork and a basic familiarity of what kinds of paperwork are required in working in a community based setting such as our clinics, however do not need to worry about the specific forms and documents until they are on the job.

DIRECT FROM THE EMPLOYERS

Discussion Questions:

1. Are there any "common themes" that run through the employers' guidance and lists for you?

2. How do you envision your work environment of the future?

3. What can you contribute as a public mental health trainee, intern or employee?

4. What do you want to know about a potential placement or work setting? What matters to you?

5. What extra skills or knowledge do you have that will make you an especially desirable candidate?

DIRECT FROM THE CONSUMERS

Recovery Oriented Care is all about consumer involvement at every level of the healthcare system. The Recovery Orientation encourages the development of a transformed culture of treatment that is inclusive, engaging, respectful and collaborative.

In the previous section, employers provided guidance for you about what they are looking for in candidates who are seeking placement or employment with them. In the next section, consumers with lived experience in the public mental health system "speak" to you.

The unedited statements that follow were received in response to our request for guidance from consumers. We asked them what they would like to experience in a treatment setting with a therapist. The statements on the pages that follow are "direct from the consumers" to you.

CONSUMER GUIDANCE

- When I visit my therapist I would like them to listen to my feelings, but also want them to talk back to me. There is nothing worse session than the therapist just sitting there and waiting for you to say something. *Renee C*

- The qualities I would like for a therapist are: To help me make wise decisions when I have a problem with clear thoughts. To make the decisions that I need to make. To be able to be understood when I need understanding and help me throughout my treatment. *Maria V*

- What would make a good therapist? A person that is sensitive to ones needs. Someone that can listen and not judge what one says. More or less a person with real and hand has a great personality. *Faith I*

- I would like to have a day with my counselor and we could have a good nice day. I would I to join a good job. *Linda B*

- I want somebody who is God centered. I need a therapist that can identify with my passion for Jesus Christ. Because I love the lord I need someone who loves the lord. *Kristen S*

- I like to see you come to help. *Michael M*

- I think talking about family problem and how to deal with hate also deal with hate and deal with different things in life. *Michelle S*

- To be heard, understood, to listen to me and understand and ask questions. *Alberto O*

WHAT I WANT IN A THERAPIST

- Approchable-calm

- A good listener- respectful of "my experience"

- Understanding

- Sincere- helps me to trust them

- Non-judgemental- does not offer a bunch of solutions, I don't have the ability to implement yet

- Offers help in the form of questions -gives me homework or skills to practice

- Treats me like an individual- is glad to see me-

- Does not minimize my feelings- ie. "oh you are Catastrophizing"

- Someone who believes in me

- Instills hope- celebrates my success

Statements on How We Want to be Treated...

Joseph C.

I am a very good man. I like to help everyone that I can. I like to play music the best I can. Talking to my family and grow them up the right way.

Christian B.

Club House: First of all I would greet them with a good morning, good afternoon, and or good evening gesture. Then, more likely I would be friendly to people because majority many people are respectful to each other. Good self-motivation, very creative and has the style of an artist.

Lydia A.

My name is Lydia . I am a consumer of the Club House, the Amazing Place. I want people to respect me, because I am a good listener, a good person, I get along with everybody. I've been coming for 12 years, I've learned to get along with people. I've learned to open up. I was shy, I am trying to not to be. I've learned to express my self. I've learned about myself, I'm an amazing person at the Amazing Place. I want to be treated like everybody else. I play cards with everybody because it's fun. I play pool, because I win. But I know winning isn't everything, its about playing, getting along with

everybody, being with your friends, laughing, having fun. I like socializing with everybody, talking, having a great time. Talking is good for everybody, we watch TV, and listen to the music. The thing I like is that I am with my friends.

LaVerne

I am confident and strong.

I am a Happy, Positive Person

I am worthy.

I am Creative and Interesting

I am Perfect. Just the way I am.

I have Healthy Personal Boundaries.

People Like to Be Around Me

Today I am Confident

I am Intelligent

I am attractive

I have a Good Circle of Friends

I accept myself For who I am

I can trust and Rely on Myself.

Vivien L.

I would like to be treated as If I didn't have a mental illness. I would hope that everyone would still have high hopes and dreams for me, because I have them. I want everyone to support me in reaching my dreams which my illness doesn't stop me from reaching. I truly believe this and I want others to believe it. I guess I just want everyone to treat me as though I didn't have a mental illness but to understand when it rears its head.

May 31, 2012

To Whom It May Concern,

I wish more people would treat me like my Medical Doctor treats me. He has a way of showing that he is concerned about my complete health. He asks questions and checks for additional problems and gives me medication to ease my symptoms. He sometimes gives me free samples to start easing my symptoms right away, and follows up with a prescription that I then take to the pharmacy. There are times when he doesn't give me medications for symptoms that I think I have, but I am okay with that because I know that he is always looking out for my best interest.

When I leave his office, I always feel much better for having made the visit. There is no doubt in my mind that I am well, or will soon be doing better...

Emilia A.

I like it when my therapist listens to me and respects what I have to say. I want them to understand me and not to rush me out of the office. – **William N.**

I like my therapist to listen to what I have to say and always tell me the truth. – *Virginia M.*

I like it when my doctor listens to me and helps me understand what meds I need and what to expect from them. – *Jerry S.*

A Letter to My Peer-Counselor Supervisor

Dear Nancy,

Here is an essay on what I think contributes to having a good qualities as a therapist, broken down by events. I hope this helps your friend.

My Life Experience and my Best Friend

I have never before received therapy from a therapist only my own support. My therapy was going through school and I analyzed myself and my life from childhood through now. I would talk to my best friend who was my therapist and she did not say much, but try and understand me by being empathetic, and listening. I would talk to get my point through, then we would have a conversation, she would give me feed back and I would listen and give her more feed back. When she would tell me what I was doing wrong, or what I should do is when I felt she was mostly wrong, because to me it did not feel right. I respected her opinion, but I do not want to do what others think I should do, unless they are willing to have a conversation on it. When my friend would give me advise and

expect me to do what she say I should do, I was not a original thought from me, and I would be giving her my right to choose, making me more unhappy.

Best Friend Scenario Therapy

Over time, I also learn that having a therapist as a friend is good, but the scenario will change. My best friend and I only go out to talk to each other and listen to each other, for dinner basically. I think my friendship with her has shifted gears in having a serious outlook to life, and the adventure side of having a friend is not there no more. That is ok for me since I do not want to have only one friend for everything, I like variety. I have my cousin who likes to travel and be spontaneous, and I am sure my best friend does the same things with her other family members and not only me.

The Qualities

Qualities that I like from my best friend who is my therapist is that she listens to me and no matter whether she likes or dislikes what she hears, she is always there to lend me her ears. I like that she is reliable source, caring, compassionate, and always expresses a welcoming feeling. I also like that we have both experienced life and she tells me some of her stories, and I give her my feedback and she listens.

The Therapy

I think cultivating respect for individual is the most important part of a therapy, because it involves the true character of a person (are they reliable, credible or not?). Over time traits, things, and other stuff seems to go weary so we have to continuously keep learning to be giving. For example, even though my best friend would advise me what choices to make, or opinionated weather she liked what she heard or not, due to respect there is a responsibility there where one comes face to face with WHO THEY ARE(in comparison to the therapist). That reality of therapy is the choices that make us WHO WE ARE, and I (the person receiving therapy) can DIFFERENTIATE the US vs. THEM. The responsibility of a choice (makes me think) then THAT IS THERAPY learning who we are, by respecting others and thinking about others and others respecting and thinking about us too.

Mayra G.

DIRECT FROM THE CONSUMERS

Discussion Questions:

1. Are there any "common themes" that run through the consumers' guidance and for you?

2. What are your personal qualities that will enable you to be especially effective in a recovery-oriented setting?

3. What should the role of consumers be in these evolving systems of care?

4. How do you feel about the consumer's expertise and a collaborative documentation process?

5. How would you organize a treatment team that includes consumer staff members?

QUICK TIPS TO STRENGTHEN THE PROVIDER-CLIENT RELATIONSHIP THROUGH CULTURAL UNDERSTANDING

SAMHSA-HRSA Center for Integrated Health Solutions

Clinicians working in integrated care settings have the best of intentions. They strive for better client engagement, better patient-provider relationships and better health and behavioral health outcomes. However, lack of cultural understanding and sensitivity are vital to engaging and caring for members of cultural, ethnic and racial groups in the care they need to achieve recovery and improved health. Below are several tips that a healthcare professional can implement today to help build stronger, more culturally competent relationships with clients of all minority populations.

- Recognize that culture is a defining characteristic for some clients, and in such, their cultural identity may be at the root of their presenting health problem.

- Alternatively, do not assume that culture is a defining characteristic of all clients. If your client views himself or herself outside the context of any cultural identity, you should too.

- Do not assure any client that you "understand." Rather than try to prove how much you know about a client's culture, demonstrate your willingness to learn from the client.

- Treat each client as an individual, not as a member of a group. People seek and need treatment, not cultures. Accept the level of importance culture takes up in a client's life and don't assume that all the characteristics you have learned are dominant in his or her culture.

- Do not assume you have an advantage with clients of the same culture as you. Your own feelings about your culture may be as much of a hindrance as a help. The feeling that you "have it right" may lead you to unknowingly force your preferences on your clients.

- Remember that human beings are more alike than different. Do not overlook obvious interpretations of behavioral health and health symptoms by only interpreting a client's actions in context of their culture.

- Accept that we all relate to others within the context of our own set of values, knowledge and experiences. In that vein, assume that you have biases and beliefs that may hinder optimal provider-client relationships. Draw upon your own expertise at the same time you honor and acknowledge each client's expertise. As an integrated

healthcare provider, you are the expert on strategies of health behavior change and treatment and services. Each of your clients is the expert on his or her own culture and the place it holds in his or her life and healthcare.

Contact CIHS for technical assistance on culturally competent care in integrated care settings.

Address: 1701 K Street NW

Suite 400

Washington, D.C. 20006

Phone: 202-684-7457

Email: integration@thenationalcouncil.org

PREPARING FOR THE FUTURE: FITTING INTO THE VISION

Ongoing state level discussions and informative presentations identify areas of competence and expertise that will be incorporated into transformed systems of care. While individual agencies and organizations will differ, the following section highlights those that are consistently named, including:

- Evidence-based Practice

- Cultural Competency

- Substance Abuse

- Trauma-informed Care

- Working with the Corrections Population

Although it is beyond the scope of this Handbook to provide detailed content related to the topics listed above, the next pages include a brief explanation followed by a list of resources for each.

CULTURAL COMPETENCE

Cultural Competence is defined as a set of congruent behaviors, attitudes and policies that come together in a system, agency or among professionals and enables that system, agency or those professionals to work effectively in cross-cultural situations (Cross et al., 1989; Issacs & Benjamin, 1991).

"Culture" refers to integrated patterns of human behavior that include the language, thoughts, communications, actions, customs, beliefs, values and institutions of racial, ethnic, religious or social groups. "Competence" implies having the capacity to function effectively as an individual and an organization within the context of the cultural beliefs, behaviors, and needs presented by consumers and their communities (Adapted from Cross, 1989).

Health care services that are responsive to and respectful of health beliefs, practices and cultural and linguistic needs of diverse patients can help to bring about positive health outcomes.

Within the Transformed Systems of Care, the concept of cultural competence is fundamental. Cultural competence is a developmental process that occurs along a continuum. Your work/placement setting may be at any point along the evolutionary continuum, however you can expect that the agency/organization's values, goals and mission statements incorporate the concept of Cultural Competency.

To Learn More about Cultural Competence:

Cross, T.L., Barzon, B.J., Dennis, K.W., & et al. (1989). Towards a culturally competent system of care: A monograph on effective services for minority children who are severely emotionally disturbed. Washington, DC; CASSP Technical Assistance Center, Georgetown University Child Development Center.

> This source gives the reader valuable information on the ways that cultures differ from one another with respect to mental illness in children and particularly violence against children within the home. It looks at different cultures and their view of child abuse and what is acceptable based on the families' background.

Pedersen, P. (1997). Culture-centered counseling interventions: Striving for accuracy. Retrieved from http://www.sagepub.com/upm-data/15654_Chapter_1.pdf

> This book excerpt would be useful to interns and trainees who are beginning to

see clients and do not have much experience working with different cultures, or those or feel overwhelmed when working with clients of differing cultures.

Griner, D. & Smith, T. B. (2006). Culturally adapted mental health interventions. *Psychotherapy: Theory, Research, Practice, Training, 43*(4), 531-548. doi:10.1037/0022-006X.59.1.12

> This research article gives examples of culturally competent interventions from the standpoint of many different schools of therapy and which ones are well balanced in cultural competence and which ones need improvement in their focus.

California Institute for Mental Health. (2002). Many voices, one direction: Building a common agenda for culturall competence in mental health. Retrieved from http://www.cimh.org/downloads/SBProceed.pdf

> This program shows the importance of why we must bring the idea of cultural competence into our training as mental health professionals so that we can effectively and ethically serve our clients. It provides materials from people of varying backgrounds so that we have insight from many cultures and the impact that mental health services has for them.

Arredondo, P. (2006). Multicultural counseling competencies = ethical practice. *Journal of Mental Health Counseling, 26*(1), 44-55.

> This is an excellent article for newcomers because it helps enforce the importance of being culturally competent and continuing to educate yourself on cultural competence to ensure that your practice is functioning ethically.

Delia, S. (2011). Cultural competency: A practical guide for mental health service providers. Retrieved from http://www.uscrirefugees.org/2010Website/5_Resources/5_3_For_Service_Providers/5_3_3_Cultural_Competency/Hogg_Foundation_for_MentalHealth.pdf

> This source gives good background information on cultural competence and what it means to be a culturally competent service provider within the mental health community.

McDonald, L., Billingham, S., Conrad, T., Morgan, A., Nancy, O., & Payton, S. (1997). Families and schools together (FAST): Integrating community development with clinical strategies. *Families in Society, 78*(2), p.140-155.

This is a useful tool for someone who is interested in working with schools and families. It shows how we can implement systems of support for children living in multicultural communities that are used in the schools but can also be used in family sessions within schools and to create psycho-education kits for communities.

Weaver, G. R. (1986). Understanding and coping with cross-cultural adjustment stress. In R. M. Paige (Ed.), Cross-Cultural Orientation, New Conceptualizations and Applications. Lanham, MD: University Press of America.

This is a great resource for clinicians who have clients who are moving to the US from other countries and are having difficulties adapting to life in the US. It gives ideas for clients to help normalize feelings and opportunities to engage the client in teaching from their point of view so that the clinician gains a better understanding of clients' culture of origin.

We Recommend

AAMFT-CA LBGT Affirmative Psychotherapy Online Certification

For more information: http://www.aamftca.org

This 36-hour CE certification is a remarkable training for clinicians everywhere. This training is designed to be an important addition to the growing field of LGBT affirmative psychotherapy and a vital service to the mental health profession and those we serve.

The certification training consists of a basic text, task force reports, journal articles, case studies, over five hours of original streaming video and material written exclusively for this curriculum. Most of the elements of the curriculum require completion of a post-test in order to move onto the next material. The 36-hour CE certification is self-paced.

Student Discount Code: **TSSTUDENT**

Save $50

SUBSTANCE ABUSE

The transforming systems of care are comprehensive, coordinated, multi-disciplinary and designed to "reattach the head to the body". It intuitively makes perfect sense to develop a comprehensive system to treat the whole person.

Similarly, within the behavioral health component of the transforming systems, substance abuse is being "reattached" to mental health. For far too long, in far too many systems of care, the phenomenal overlap between substance abuse and mental health was not acknowledged, particularly in the funding streams and billing categories. Therapy was provided for mental health services, while individuals were referred out to "twelve step" programs to focus on their substance abuse issues. Substance abuse counselors often had different education and training, frequently becoming credentialed through a two-year college program, supplemented by "lived experience" on the streets. While mental health providers respected their process and sometimes actively coordinated with the substance abuse counselors, they often conveyed some sense of professional/clinical superiority.

As the prevalence of co-occurring disorders became increasing recognized, education and training in working with issues of substance abuse has been established as a standard, basic competency for mental health providers. In transforming systems of care the "caste system" is virtually demolished, as mental health and substance abuse providers share equal footing within the larger concept of Behavioral Health Care.

As a mental health provider, you are more marketable and valuable within the system if you have acquired additional training and certification in working with issues of substance abuse.

To Learn More About Substance Abuse:

Substance Abuse and Mental Health Services Administration. (2005). KAP keys for clinicians based on TIP 42. Retrieved from: http://store.samhsa.gov/product/Substance-Abuse-Treatment-for-Persons-With-Co-Occurring-Disorders/SMA08-4036

> KAP Keys for Clinicians series can be downloaded for free by the reader directly from the site. Each guide gives specific tools for each subject. This Key focuses on co-occurring disorders and provides techniques on assessment and treatment for clients with substance abuse disorders. The step-by-step guides are particularly helpful for trainees who are unfamiliar with the assessment phase of working with clients with co-occurring disorders.

Nace, E. & Tinsley, J. (2007). *Patients with substance abuse problems: Effective identification, diagnosis, and treatment.* Norton. New York, NY.

> This book gives students a look at substance abuse disorders in clients of all ages and walks students through the complete journey of substance abuse treatment from the initial assessment through treatment goals and outcomes.

Ford, J. H., II, Green, C. A., Hoffman, K. A., Wisdom, J. P., Riley, K. J., Bergmann, L., & Molfenter, T. (2007). Process improvement needs in substance abuse treatment: Admissions walk-through results. *Journal of Substance Abuse Treatment, 33*(44), 379-389.

> This article provides the reader with step-by-step instructions on how to improve patient interactions during treatment. It shows flaws in currently used programs and gives ideas on ways that we can better assist our clients.

Dennis, M., Titus, J., White, M., Unsicker, J. & Hodgkins, D. (2003). Global appraisal of individual needs (GAIN): Administration guide for the GAIN and related measures (version 5). Retrieved from http://www.chestnut.org/LI/gain/index.html#Administration%20Manual

> This manual will show students how to use the GAIN assessment tool for clients with substance abuse and help the student become more familiar with its usefulness as a way to engage the client in the process of substance abuse treatment.

Hanes-Stevens, L. & White, K. (2008). Effective treatment planning for substance abuse and related disorders. Retrieved from http://www.readingetc.com/counselormagazine/feature-articles-mainmenu-63/27-treatment-strategies-or-protocols/817-effective-treatment-planning-for-substance-abuseand-related-disorders

> This article highlights the need for effective treatment planning for individuals with substance use disorders. The article teaches how clinicians should match the treatment goals to the treatment plan and what tools are useful for clients and what aren't. The article also gives a good list of do's and don'ts which are an easy access tip for newcomers.

Adolescent Trauma and Substance Abuse Committee of the National Child Traumatic Stress Network (2008). Understanding the links between adolescent trauma and substance abuse: A toolkit for providers. Retrieved from http://www.nctsnet.org/sites/default/files/assets/pdfs/satoolkit_providerguide.pdf

This is a toolkit for readers that helps highlight the factors of childhood trauma and substance abuse. It gives practical ideas about what clinicians should be aware of and look for during assessments to identify underlying issues contributing to substance abuse.

McDonald, L. and Sayger T. (1998). Impact of a family and school-based prevention program on protective factors for high risk youth: Issues in evaluation. In J. Valentine , N. Kennedy, J. de Jong, (Eds.). *Substance abuse prevention in multicultural communities.* New York: Hayworth Press.

This source gives solid information on the unique aspects of working with multi-cultural communities to preventing substance abuse. It offers the reader insight on the ways different cultures view substance abuse and how and why young children become involved in substance use.

WE RECOMMEND:

AAMFT-CA/MATRIX INSTITUTE Substance Use Disorder Online Certification

For more information: http://www.aamftca.org

Providers will find this certification training to be a valuable addition to their clinical repertoires. This curriculum is a combined effort by two highly respected training organizations: AAMFT-CA and The Matrix Institute. This 20-CE hour certification includes seven hours of original streaming video, is a remarkable training and continuing education opportunity for statewide clinicians of all licensure and for the profession as a whole. We believe that it will be a vital service to both clinicians and those we serve.

Student Discount Code: **TSSTUDENT**

Save $50

EVIDENCE-BASED PRACTICE

Evidence-based practice (EBP) was first developed within the context of medical clinical assessment. To earn the title of "evidence-based," a practice must be grounded in consistent research findings. EBPs are interventions for which there is consistent, scientific evidence shown to improve specifically identified client outcomes for specific targeted populations (Drake et. al, 2001). They are standardized, replicable and effective.

As applied to mental health treatment, evidence-based practice has surfaced as an attempt to respectfully bring 'science to services." The National Institute of Medicine defines evidence-based practice as "....the integration of the best research evidence with clinical expertise and patient values." This definition serves to clarify that evidence-based practices involve the incorporation of research with, not in lieu of, clinical expertise and client values/choice. In mental health treatment, EBP refers to the process of using empirical data to make decisions about how to best care for the client. However, the strategic, decision making process in evidence-based practice honors the skills and knowledge of the therapist as well as the desires and values of the client.

The limits of evidence-based practice are clearly delineated in the research, centering on the stipulation that all factors be replicated in order to achieve the same result. Such limits have led researchers to define a hierarchy of scientific evidence, including: effective and efficacious practices; promising and emerging practices; and evidence-based thinking. Adequate documentation of the effectiveness of the therapeutic encounter remains a struggle. The process is slow, but progress is being made. In recent years, community mental health in California has incorporated the use of specific evidence-based practices, which can provide a structure for documenting outcome and effectiveness in response to funding requirements related to measuring change.

To Learn More about Evidence-based Practice:

Dobson, K., & Craig, K. (1998). *Empirically supported therapies: Best practice in professional psychology.* Thousand oaks, CA: Sage

> This book offers varied approaches of evidence-based practices to help students understand different theories and methods that can be used when working with clients.

Gibbs, L. (2003). *Evidence-based practice for the helping professions.* New York: Wadsworth.

Gilgun, J. (2006). The four cornerstones of qualitative research. *Qualitative Health Research, 16*(3), 436-443.

> Helpful for research based courses where students need to evaluate research articles based on techniques used in the studies.

Stout, C., & Hayes, R. (Eds.). (2005). **The evidenced-based practice: Methods, models and tools for mental health professionals.** Hoboken, NJ: Wiley.

> This resource provides detailed methods, models and tools that students may find useful in practicum and in classes. The methods outlined give students ideas about working with clients and how to evaluate their outcomes.

Surface, D. (2009). Understanding evidence-based practice in behavioral health. *Social Work Today. 9*(4) P. 22

Wampold, B. (2007). Psychotherapy: The humanistic and (effective) treatment. *American Psychologist, 62*(8), pp.857-873.

> This article looks at the need for a balance between humanistic approaches to therapy that are also evidence-based.

TRAUMA-INFORMED CARE

What is Trauma-Informed Care?

Most individuals seeking public behavioral health services and many other public services, such as homeless and domestic violence services have histories of physical and sexual abuse and other types of trauma-inducing experiences. These experiences often lead to mental health and co-occurring disorders such as chronic health conditions, substance abuse, eating disorders, and HIV/AIDS, as well as contact with the criminal justice system.

When a human service program takes the step to become trauma-informed, every part of its organization, management, and service delivery system is assessed and potentially modified to include a basic understanding of how trauma affects the life of an individual seeking services. Trauma-informed organizations, programs, and services are based on an understanding of the vulnerabilities or triggers of trauma survivors that traditional service delivery approaches may exacerbate, so that these services and programs can be more supportive and avoid re-traumatization.

What are Trauma-Specific Interventions?

Trauma-specific interventions are designed specifically to address the consequences of trauma in the individual and to facilitate healing. Treatment programs generally recognize the following:

- The survivor's need to be respected, informed, connected, and hopeful regarding their own recovery

- The interrelation between trauma and symptoms of trauma (e.g., substance abuse, eating disorders, depression, and anxiety)

- The need to work in a collaborative way with survivors, family and friends of the survivor, and other human services agencies in a manner that will empower survivors and consumers

*Taken from SAMSHA: http://www.samhsa.gov/nctic/trauma.asp

Your understanding of and familiarity with the concepts and interventions related to Trauma-informed Care will be appreciated and acknowledged in the transforming systems of care.

To Learn More about Trauma-informed Care:

Elliot, D., Bjelajac, P., Fallot, R., Markoff, L., & Glover Reed, B. (2005). Trauma-informed or trauma-denied: Principles and implementation of trauma-informed services for women. *Journal of Community Psychology. 33*(4), 461-477.

> This article provides a clear outline of the specifics of trauma-informed treatment and how it can be used effectively to treat women in crisis. It also provides examples of services available for those in need and focuses on outreach and engagement of clients.

Fallot, R.D. & Harriss, M. (2002). *Trauma-informed services: A self-assessment and planning protocol.* Washington, D.C; Community Connections.

> This resource is helpful for those in the beginning stages of traineeships or practice planning in that it offers the reader a method of setting up an environment for trauma-informed services. It provides useful information on how to incorporate trauma-informed treatment into your client sessions both individually and in group settings.

de Arellano, M. A., Ko, S.J., Danielson, C. K. & Sprague, C.M. (2008). *Trauma-informed interventions: Clinical and research evidence and culture-specific information project.* Los Angeles, CA & Durham, NC: National Center for Child Traumatic Stress.

> This is a great resource for those who need research articles and/or statistics to back up an argument. This resource provides many different research projects that have been performed with children and provides concrete statistics for all studies.

Hopper, E.K., Bassuk, E.L. & Olivet, J. (2010). Shelter from the storm: Trauma-informed care in homelessness services settings. *The Open Health Services and Policy Journal. 3*, 80-100.

> This article focuses on the homeless population and the unique set of circumstances of trauma that lead many into homelessness. It stresses the importance of recognizing the factors that create trauma for homeless individuals including the idea that homelessness itself is traumatizing and can lead to victimization and re-traumatization.

Grubaugh, A.L., Zinzow, H.M., Paul, L. & et al. (2011). Trauma exposure and posttraumatic stress disorder in adults with severe mental illness: a critical review. *Clinical Psychology Review, 31*(6). 883–899.

> This article shows the link between trauma exposure and PTSD and the additional effects that the original trauma can have on a mentally ill patient. It provides solid treatment advice particularly helpful to those who are just beginning to incorporate trauma-informed treatment into their work with clients.

Campbell, M. & Morrison, A. (2007). The psychological consequences of combat exposure: The importance of appraisals and post-traumatic stress disorder symptomatology in the occurrence of delusional-like ideas. *British Journal of Clinical Psychology 46*(2). 187–201.

> With so many clients returning from combat or have previously served in armed forces who continue to need care, this is an important resource for those working with the VA population. It gives insight on how the client views his or her circumstances, how that view came to be and how to help the client work through PTSD without re-traumatizing the client in the process.

Child Sexual Abuse Task Force and Research Practice Core, National Child Traumatic Stress Network. (2004). *How to implement trauma-focused cognitive behavioral therapy.* Durham, NC and Los Angeles, CA: National Center for Child Traumatic Stress.

> This handbook offers the reader specific steps to implement the use of T-F CBT when working with children. It helps readers understand which clients are good candidates for T-F CBT and also gives helpful ideas about timelines for the therapeutic relationship.

Covington, S. (2008). Women and addiction: A trauma-informed approach. *Journal of Psychoactive Drugs*, SARC Supplement 5, 377-385.

> This article focuses on the difference in treatment of men with addictions versus women with addictions and the need for gender specific treatment models. The model the author suggests incorporates three areas: trauma, addiction and relational-cultural theories.

WORKING WITH THE CORRECTIONS POPULATION

In 2011, Governor Brown proposed, and the Legislature passed, prison realignment legislation to ease prison crowding and reduce the department's budget. This legislation created and funded a community-based correctional program where lower-level offenders remain under the jurisdiction of county governments. After the initial six months that realignment was in effect, the approximately 22,000 inmates were released into their communities.

Low-level offenders often struggle with issues related to homelessness, drug treatment and mental illness. Working with this population within community mental health settings can be very fitting for the Marriage and Family Therapists' traditional training in systemic and relationship work. The funding is in the communities and opportunities for employment in these specialized programs are increasing. You can potentially be more marketable in community mental health if you have gone "beyond the call" to increase your knowledge and skills in working with the corrections population.

To Learn More:

Sampl, S., Wakai, S., & Trestman, R.L. (2010). Translating evidence-based practices from community to corrections: An example of implementing DBT-CM. *Journal of Behavioral Analysis of Offender and Victim Treatment and Prevention, 2*(2). 114-23.

> This article offers insight into how and why DBT is an effective treatment for the corrections population, especially how it focuses the client in reflecting on past events and how the client can more effectively handle those problematic situations both in the present and future.

Shelton, D. (2010). Design, test and implementation of an evidence-based treatment intervention for incarcerated persons with behavioral problems". International Association of Forensic Nurses. 18TH Annual Scientific Assembly, Oct.27-30, 2010, Pittsburg, PA.

Vlach , D. L. & Daniels, A. E. (2007). Commentary: Evolving toward equivalence in correctional mental health care—a view from the maximum security trenches. *J Am Acad Psychiatry Law, 35*(4). 436-8.

> This article is written by a worker in a maximum security institution and provides excellent insight from someone who is working with the corrections population on a daily basis and understands the need for laws to protect prisoners with mental illnesses and the obstacles that surround the availability

of such services. It also shows the needs of the mental health professional providing services and how they are unique from the needs of those serving other populations.

Pinta, E. (2010). Introduction to mental health treatment in corrections: A clinician's perspective. Civic Research Institute, Inc. Kingston, NJ.

Although this book is written by a Psychiatrist it provides useful materials for all mental health professionals. It breaks down various issues one may encounter in the corrections field including suicide prevention, violent clients, and prevalence rates amongst the corrections population. It is a useful tool for one just beginning to work with the corrections population as it has many sections that focus on the differing culture within a prison from the outside.

Lamb, H. R. & Weinberger, L. (2011). Meeting the needs of those persons with serious mental illness who are most likely to become criminalized. *Journal of the American Academy of Psychiatry and the Law Online, 39*(4). 549-554.

This article discusses how we formerly cared for those with mental illnesses and how we presently care for them and focuses on the need for specialized care for those with mental illnesses. It particularly focuses on how we can prevent those with serious mental illnesses from becoming criminalized and being introduced into the prison system.

Admas, K. & Ferrandino, J. (2008). Managing mentally ill inmates in prisons. *Criminal Justice and Behavior, 35*(8). 913-927.

This article focuses on the possible future of managing mental illness with the corrections population and what we can do now to help foster a system that provides the correct balance of work between mental health professionals and corrections officers. It offers a look at how the two professional fields are trained and how the differ and in effect negate one another in terms of benefits to the mentally ill inmate.

Knight, P., Phillips, A., Underwood, L. & von Dresner, K. (2006). Critical factors in mental health programming for juveniles in corrections facilities. *International Journal of Behavioral Consultation and Therapy, 2*(1). 107-131.

> This article effectively underlines the unique issues of managing mental illnesses in the juvenile corrections population and how those differ from adults within the corrections department. The article points to the need for juveniles to receive treatment for their mental illness in addition to psychoeducation and tools so the juvenile does not become an adult offender.

Altschuler, D. M. (1999). Trends and issues in the adultification of juvenile justice. In Research To Results: Effective Community Corrections, edited by P. Harris.

Lanham, MD: American Correctional Association.

> This resource shows the trends of mentally ill juveniles who are incarcerated throughout their childhood and follow the same path into adulthood. It focuses on the need to disrupt the cycle the individual follows that ultimately leads him or her to re-offend.

CONCLUDING THOUGHTS

This handbook is dedicated to persons living with mental illness and reflects the contributors' commitment to the recovery model as an innovative approach to treatment. It is our hope that this Handbook will contribute to better lives for consumers and encourage community and collaboration among those who work with them. Our ongoing work on this project embodies the collaborative spirit we bring to the task; therefore, we plan to update the Handbook regularly as we gain greater understanding of the recovery model and its application in the real world.